OCCUPATION NURSE

First edition, published in 2001 by

WOODFIELD PUBLISHING
Woodfield House, Babsham Lane, Bognor Regis
West Sussex PO21 5EL, England.

ISBN 1-873203-96-9

ISBN 1-873203-96-9

9 781873 203965

Occupation
Nurse

Nursing in Guernsey 1940-1945

PETER & MARY
BIRCHENALL

Woodfield Publishing
~WEST SUSSEX • ENGLAND ~

The States of Guernsey Emergency Hospital 1940 (above). Note the second floor balcony where patients received nursing care in the open air.

Contents

About the authors

Peter and Mary Birchenall trained as nurses in the 1960s. Peter is a professor of Health Studies and Mary is a senior lecturer in Nursing at a northern University. They live in a small village on the outskirts of York.

This book is dedicated to those nurses across the world who care for people whose lives are blighted by war, famine and oppression.

Members of the Nursing Staff c1940
Nurse Miller, Nurse Webber, Nurse Point
Nurse Leale, Nurse LeLevier, Nurse Longlais, Nurse Toms

Preface

Throughout almost all of World War II the Channel Islands were placed under military occupation by forces of the Third Reich (1940-1945). To all intents and purposes the islanders were left to their own devices and for five long dark years they were forced to make a life for themselves under the oppressive shadow of the swastika. As may be imagined, this period in the history of these islands produced many stories of personal suffering, courage and dogged resistance. Also, there are stories laced with ironic humour that serve to illustrate the strength of the human spirit, no matter how bleak the circumstances may have been.

Among the islanders was a group of people, mainly young unqualified women, who were dedicated to nursing the sick and injured civilian population of Guernsey during its Occupation. Theirs is a remarkable story of providing a health service without proper resources or any real training. Under the disciplined but humane leadership of three qualified matrons they turned the philosophy of 'make do and mend' into an art form. These young women, many then still in their teens and early twenties, were exposed to situations and long hours of duty that made huge demands on their resilience, stamina and dedication to duty. There was no formally organised counselling service, their support came from each other and they just 'got on with it'. It is in the face of such adversity that lifelong friendships are forged, and even though bodies may age with the passing of time, youthful memories remain clear and uncluttered. This book became possible through the willingness of surviving nurses to share their memories, thus providing us with a rare opportunity to experience nursing life in a small island hospital under wartime conditions.

Foreword

I felt honoured when invited by Peter and Mary Birchenall to write the foreword to a book that gives the reader valuable insight into the many personal memories and strength of comradeship experienced by Guernsey nurses during times of adversity and severe hardship. This is a well-researched and accurate account of the traumatic years of German Occupation, which had a major impact on health-care delivery in Guernsey. Anaesthetics, antibiotics, insulin and dressings soon became scarce and a number of deaths resulted when insulin supplies ran short. During the early stage of the Occupation, representatives travelled to France in an effort to obtain essential supplies of food and medicines: consequently, strict food rationing was introduced. Malnutrition soon led to people being hospitalised for what would normally have been minor illnesses.

The States of Guernsey met the need for an Emergency Hospital through consolidating existing hospital services onto a single site, managed by three Matrons. We see how Matron Rabey soon emerged as the dominant personality. Guernsey had no formal nursing training and registered nurses were recruited from the mainland or were local women who had undertaken their training in the UK. However, many of the local women recruited to the Emergency Hospital were nursing assistants, lacking in experience but not in enthusiasm to learn. Guernsey remained isolated, staff were denied access to publications, journals, new developments in nursing and medicine and, therefore, were forced to rely on time-honoured techniques. Occasionally, medical staff would agree to give lectures during the evening, and as the nurses were required to reside in the adjacent nurses' home, the curfew restrictions ensured that these sessions were well attended.

Fractures and minor injuries occurred due to road accidents when the occupying forces insisted all vehicles travel on the right-hand side of the road. The theatre sister acted as the surgeons' assistant when a supply of anaesthetics was available, however, the incorrect size and type of suturing material, and the unavailability of dressings and cotton wool, led to many wound-site infections. Appeals through the local press for linen bought about some interesting substitute materials. Nurses recall the need to exercise their imagination and how they became skilful in the use of alternatives. Peter and Mary Birchenall treat us to many anecdotes – some amusing and some sad – which collectively bring to life the uniqueness of working as a nurse during the Occupation.

Among the saddest of these reflections is the tragedy of a young Jewish Austrian woman, Therese Steiner, who fled her war-torn homeland and was employed by an English family as an au pair. At the outbreak of war she found herself stranded on Sark where the family were on holiday. Being considered by the Home Office as a foreign national she was prevented from returning with the family to their home in Essex. She moved to Guernsey and worked as a nursing assistant at the

Emergency Hospital. Her three years in Guernsey came to an abrupt end when she was deported to Auschwitz where she was put to death.

Five years of Occupation took their toll on the inner resources of the nursing and medical staff. The liberation allowed some relief when four Canadian St. John's Ambulance volunteer nurses were recruited to the hospital. Their contribution to the service was greatly appreciated by hard-pressed staff and their patients.

During a visit to Canada in June 1997, I presented a conference paper on Nursing during the Occupation. Whilst there, I was privileged to deliver a personal letter to the Chancellor of the St John Ambulance Service in Ottawa, from the Bailiff of Guernsey, recognising and extending thanks for the dedicated contribution of those four nurses.

Peter and Mary Birchenall not only describe nursing during the Occupation but also provide a permanent record of events, covering a period of Guernsey's history, which is both interesting and unique.

Sandra James
Senior Nurse
Catel Hospital
Guernsey
May 2001

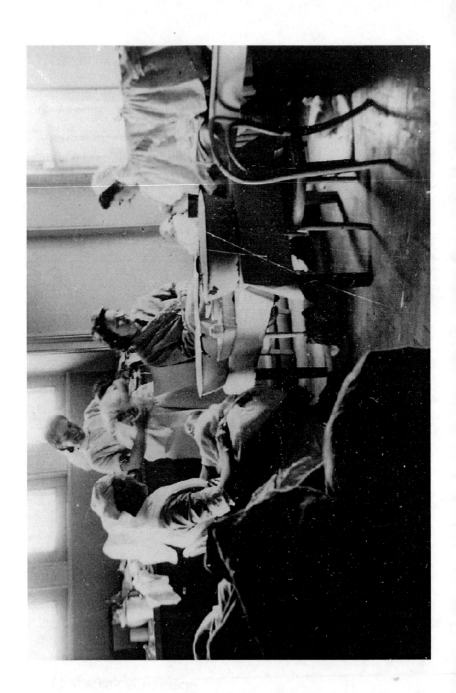

Introduction

This book owes its existence to two apparently unconnected
chance events, the first in Jersey, and the second in Guernsey.
The build up to these coincidences began with the knowledge that May 9th 1995 was a landmark date in Channel
Island history. It marked the 50th anniversary of the
Liberation of the islands from German military occupation.
Many activities were being planned to celebrate this
momentous occasion, including a royal visit from the Prince
of Wales. In the year preceding this anniversary we spent our
Summer holiday in Jersey, lazily touring the island, visiting
places of interest, speaking to people and seeing for ourselves
the preparations that were already in hand for the following
year. It was in the Parish of St Clement that we accepted an
invitation to contribute in a very small way to the completion
of one of the panels that was to make up the Island's
Occupation Tapestry. The village hall was buzzing with
industry, we heard stories of life during the Occupation that
prompted our decision to return the following May to witness

(opposite) **The Maternity Ward**
Nurse Jean Ozanne (seated) Nurse Beryl Hocart and baby (standing),
Mother (seated), Nurse Mary Harvey bathing and dressing baby.

the parades and speeches during this significant week; we just wanted to be part of it.

True to our word, we returned to Jersey in May 1995. It was part of our experience to attend a Church service at St Paul's in St Helier where members of the congregation gave short presentations about where they were and what they had been doing at the time the liberating troops had arrived on the Island. It was here that the first chance event occurred. One of these presentations was given by a lady who began with the phrase, '*I was stood with my nursing colleagues...*' As one, we turned to each other and voiced the same idea; here was a story that needed to be told. This fascinating story of nursing in an occupied country could entertain and inform today's nurse as well as provide a significant element in the foundation and history of modern nursing.

In August 1995 we travelled to Guernsey, and yet more accounts were to follow. The second chance event happened over a cup of coffee in Creasey's Department Store, overlooking St Peter Port harbour. Sat at the next table was a Guernsey man who overheard our enthusiastic discussion regarding nursing during the Occupation – we talked of nothing else. He put us in touch with Beryl Ozanne, who had recently published her own book, 'A Peep Behind the Screens', a copy of which he had in his car. This generous man gave us the book, which was read avidly that evening. Wishing to waste no further time in capitalising on this remarkable coincidence we contacted Beryl by telephone the following morning, when a meeting was arranged. Right from our first contact this delightful woman treated us very well. As will be seen later, Beryl's willingness to seek out other island wartime nurses who would share their experiences led to her becoming a cornerstone of our research.

We spent three days during October of that year collecting memories from former nurses, touring the site of the hospital, and have busily immersed ourselves in the life and times of Guernsey under Occupation ever since.

We are eternally grateful to the small band of generous and gracious people who gave us so much of their time and wish to acknowledge them individually:

Barbara Broadbent	Barbara Duport
Brenda Herve	Beryl Hocart
Osmond Gallienne	Phil Mahy
Marge Martel	Barbara Newman
Mary Ogier	Beryl Ozanne
Melva Stacey	

This story is essentially theirs and documents a significant contribution to the nurturing of the people of Guernsey during those years 1940-1945. In the chapters that follow, the health care of the islanders unfolds, told through the memories of the people who were there. Memories that other published accounts and archived records demonstrate as accurate, as though the significance of those years have been engraved on crystal.

A PLAN OF ACTION

This book is the story of nursing during the wartime Occupation of Guernsey. The nurses concerned worked in the specially created Emergency Hospital located within the Parish of Catel. Sadly, it is not everyone's memories that have been captured here, because as the introduction informs you, the development of the book waited fifty years and only some members of that hearty brigade of women and men could be found. Needless to say, it was the youngest of the groups of nurses and helpers who survived into the present day, for some of the more senior staff had died in recent years. So the nurses who informed our research in those war years were often new into the profession and would probably have been students in training had the circumstances permitted. This section outlines the process through which we gleaned the information that forms the foundation of the book.

RESEARCH

Research can seem a somewhat heavy concept for the average reader. It is important to ensure that the material outlined in this book is more than entertainment. The stories and facts given throughout have been subject to a rigorous process. Oral History is a recognised research strategy described by Baum (1970) as 'A way of taking down reminiscences by means of a tape recorder, not random reminiscences but planned interviews on a subject of historical interest about which the narrator can speak with authority.' This describes exactly the process in which we engaged while investigating the history of nursing in Occupied Guernsey. The tale that unfolds is focused on the lives of ten women and one man in their youth. This section tells something about them as they are now, and also provides you with an insight into the rigour with which the memories of a particular group were uncovered and interpreted.

BERYL OZANNE

Researchers seeking to interpret the understandings of individuals need someone to help them find the right people and to introduce them – a gatekeeper. For us, Beryl became our gatekeeper. Through the medium of her own book she had started the process of organising personal memories of her years as a wartime nurse. During the initial meeting with Beryl we demonstrated a genuine honesty in our desire to record for posterity a collective wartime nursing experience. Together we collated a list of possible interviewees and the early stages of organising the research began to take shape. However, before moving into this, the first meeting with Beryl has its own significance. Having arranged an appointment to meet with her, it was our concern to make a good impression. Because they were celebrating the fiftieth anniversary of their liberation, the Channel Islands were much in the news. As a consequence any investigators were treated with caution as some journalists had caused painful circumstances to be misconstrued, leaving many Islanders with a distaste for any outsiders professing an interest in their wartime history. We arrived at Beryl's cottage to be met by her family who surrounded her, resembling a virtual protective wall. They

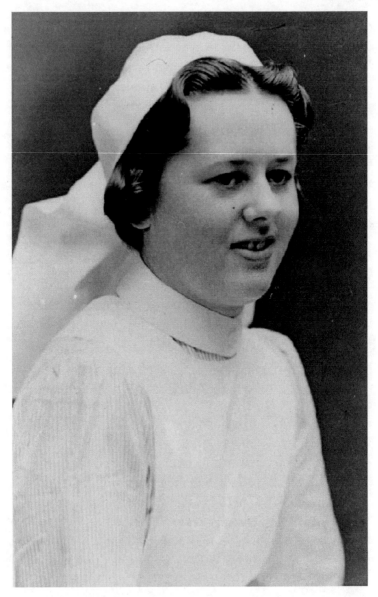

Nurse Beryl Ozanne (nee Lucas) – June 1941.

were obviously anxious to ensure that she was not bullied in any way by these mainland academics or that we would abuse her writings. A critical moment overcome, we believe, by our genuine enthusiasm and Beryl's infectious good humour and courtesy. That first meeting was a monumental step in establishing this project as without the insights, contacts and introductions provided by Beryl this research would have been a very different enterprise.

Beryl accessed her network of friends and located the names, addresses and telephone numbers of approximately 17 people who had worked in the Emergency Hospital during the war years. From that list we wrote to individuals, following up by telephone where possible. The real sergeant major here was of course Beryl herself, who found the challenge of helping us entertaining and hopefully enjoyable. Despite her own poor health she kept us informed of who was coming and how people were receiving the idea of being interviewed.

THE VENUE

Knowing that we would have a list of people to interview, a venue was required and as visitors to the Island we had no base to carry out the interviews. Although it would have been possible to hire a hotel seminar room, this was far from the best option, so we investigated the possibility of using a hospital office. The continued existence of Catel hospital, the previous Emergency Hospital, was an unlooked for bonus. The optimum site had to be the very place that Beryl and her colleagues had nursed during the war. The senior managers of Catel hospital found the nature of this research interesting.

They offered to provide a room and refreshments for the three days over which the interviews were planned.

The decision to invite our respondents to the hospital proved to be sound, as all were willing if not able to come to this venue full of memories. For some this was to be their first visit to the hospital since the war ended. There were many ways in which the overall layout of the hospital had changed since 'their day'. These changes provoked excited discussion, triggering the intriguing process of reliving those unforgettable years of their lives.

Once settled in, the office in the hospital continued to remind people in subtle ways of life back in those early years of the 1940's. It provided them with a common focus that was to prove more significant than we had ever imagined because, with few exceptions, they had not met since those eventful wartime days. Becoming engrossed in the nature of the changes in the hospital provided a common subject for conversation that eased early tensions.

We are grateful for the assistance of the hospital management who not only provided the room, but also ample supplies of tea and coffee that kept everyone refreshed.

THE INTERVIEWS

Group interviews were selected as the most appropriate strategy for achieving the aims of the research. The nature of the group task being to focus on the memories of their wartime experiences of nursing in the Emergency Hospital. Interviewing people in groups has the advantage of ensuring that individuals do not feel exposed or stressed by the research situation. Certainly, once the groups met and sat round the table they found that they could remember far more than initially expected. After all, we were asking them to go back fifty years and as some quipped, remembering what they had had for breakfast was fraught with difficulties! Nonetheless, they soon found themselves in buoyant mood, reminiscing about the Occupation and their nursing lives.

Maintaining some semblance of structure seemed prohibitive, but in reality the tales of nursing work, hospital structures and the nature of their lives, both professional and personal provided a pattern that avoided random and unconnected stories. The first interview began with formal introductions, as the nurses became re-aquainted. Once refreshments were served, the magic of memory prompted a sense of excitement, quickly followed by good-natured banter. This first interview encouraged a free flow of memories, resulting in a butterfly flit from subject to subject. Encouraged by the range of potential topics we established areas for development that would be clarified and expanded in the next round of interviews.

The Guernsey States Archive also helped in the clarifying process, providing us with the detail for issues such as nurses' salaries that were difficult for our interviewees to remember with precision after all these years. Interviews two and three followed a similar pattern, although the introduction became mellower as the former nurses reassured each other of the naturalness of the process. We felt it was important to establish a relaxed and ordinary or natural atmosphere, and after the first few minutes of each interview it was evident that the former nurses were having a sound reminiscence that echoed the pattern of an ordinary conversation.

They found themselves prompting each other into memories that had remained dormant for many years. Occasionally, one person would regale us with a tale about another, who denied all knowledge of the event. Minutes later they would corroborate and enlarge upon the story as the process of association jogged their memories. To assist with the piecing together of all the information from the interviews, we had recourse to the Island's archive, libraries and museums.

ARCHIVE (PUBLIC AND PERSONAL)

Guernsey has a very helpful States Archive Office. Here we found the records of the organising committees responsible for the Emergency Hospital and many other artefacts that corroborated the stories of these former nurses. Sometimes we would come across something in the archive that was useful to follow up in the interviews, such as soap shortages and food rationing. Occasionally, it was not possible to find exact information, as in the number of beds in the hospital.

The time spent in the archive could sound dismal and perhaps dusty. Nothing could be further from reality: the documents, when linked to the real stories of the nurses, came alive. This was an interesting time, a period that ended too quickly. The ledgers of minutes, written in copperplate handwriting, using pen and ink, with few errors, were in themselves an experience not to be missed. Thinking in terms of history, and perhaps researchers looking back on the present day, it seems unlikely that anyone will touch a computer screen and feel the awe that filled us when opening these books. Certainly, the photocopies of the pages that we didn't have time to read do not have the same inspiration as the originals.

The States Archive Office provided us with much that was factual; a sense of the organisation of the hospital and the island during the Occupation was gained from reading the factual accounts of day to day management issues. Linking the official and the nursing accounts is our other source of archive material. The nurses provided us with photographs, notebooks, copies of letters and wage slips, hoarded in boxes, hidden and forgotten. The photographs prompted further memories and helped to bring to life the heroes and heroines of that time. The lecture notes, carefully preserved, opened an avenue of understanding into the pride and care that nurses of that time took in their learning. The Priaulx Library, St Peter Port, made relevant newspaper reports available to us. The colour and atmosphere, so essential to appreciating the reality of the time was experienced through several visits to the absorbing Guernsey Occupation Museum.

The interviews and the archive provided essential evidence for these tales of nursing during the years of Occupation. The unravelling of these tales occurred after extensive immersion in the transcripts of the interviews. The need to make sense of the total story and provide a succinct account for others to read meant that some thematic structure had to be identified. Developing themes from transcripts of interviews can follow a given pattern and one such is termed the 'constant comparative method'. But even using such a complex strategy does not ensure that the researchers are remaining true to the stories told by their subjects. Therefore, a return to Guernsey to share the themes and show some of the interpretation from the taped interviews was a necessity.

Again, Beryl was the first port of call where she discussed with us the many ideas emerging from our interview transcripts. This was an opportunity for names to be corrected, spellings checked, factual details verified and amendments made. The themes that had been identified from the tapes were agreed as valid. We could now return to the computer with energy and enthusiasm to write up this story with the knowledge that the memories of a significant group of people, who had worked as nurses during the occupation of Guernsey by Germany, were represented in this book with authenticity.

~ I ~

Setting the Scene

Nurse Helen Duquemin with Joyce Kirby in the Hospital garden, 1941.

B Y THE END OF APRIL 1940, Hitler's army had overrun Norway and Denmark. With remarkable speed a similar fate befell Holland, Belgium and France. By the 21st of May 1940, German spearheads had reached the Channel at Boulogne. The fearful spectre of invasion had become a reality to the British government, so British and French troops moved into Belgium to form a desperate last line of resistance. Faced with overwhelming odds Brussels and Antwerp fell to the advancing German army with Belgium's ruling monarchy capitulating on the 28th May.

Under heavy, relentless enemy gunfire, British and French troops were pinned into the small coastal area of Dunkirk. It seemed their fate was sealed as soldiers caught on the open beach fell beneath a withering hail of bullets. Were it not for the combined gallantry of the Royal Navy, the Royal Air Force, and the extraordinary bravery of thousands of volunteers manning an armada of 'little ships' many more would have perished. It is to their everlasting credit that over 335,000 Allied troops were evacuated across the channel to safety. By now, through their binoculars, triumphant German generals had a clear view of the British coast. This held dreadful consequences for the Channel Islands as Hitler's troops were only a 'stones throw' away.

Because of the close proximity of German forces to Guernsey, as well as its neighbouring islands, the vulnerability to enemy Occupation was recognised. The islanders took some reassurance from the presence of a small military force consisting of army personnel and a number of strategically placed anti-aircraft guns. Beryl Ozanne, relates in her book 'A Peep Behind the Screens' how everyone considered themselves very lucky to be living in such a beautiful environment untouched by the ravages of the European conflict. Even though Guernsey people were aware of the war raging only a few short miles from their shores, they did not really expect to be directly involved. Indeed, why should Hitler be concerned with a small group of islands offering minimal strategic value? So shipping of goods to and from the British mainland carried on, as did life in general. Suddenly, the army and anti-aircraft guns were removed from the island to be deployed elsewhere, effectively leaving Guernsey demilitarised and undefended. His Majesty King George VI sent a message to the Bailiffs of Jersey and Guernsey that read as follows:

> 'For strategic reasons it has been found necessary to withdraw the Armed Forces from the Channel Islands. I deeply regret this necessity and I wish to assure my people in the Islands that in taking this decision, My Government has not been unmindful of their position. It is in their interest that this step should be taken in present circumstances. The long association of the Islands with the Crown and the loyal service the people of the Islands have rendered to my ancestors and Myself are guarantees that the link between us will remain unbroken and I know that My people in the Islands will look forward with the same confidence as I do to the day when the resolute fortitude with which we face our present difficulties will reap the reward of victory.'
>
> GEORGE RI

Guernsey became known as an 'open town' and in his review of the Occupation written in 1945, Jurat John Leale wrote:

> 'The British Government had deemed that the stern demands of that time had made it necessary to throw open the Island to the German invader should he care to come. We stood on the threshold of events not only previously undreamed of by any of us, but unprecedented in our history'

EVACUATION FROM GUERNSEY

The situation made it necessary for the Island authorities to take stern measures that would, as far as possible safeguard the lives of Guernsey's children. On the 19th June 1940, an announcement was made that would result in the evacuation of many children of school age to mainland Britain, to be placed in the care of surrogate families. Along with the children others were offered the chance of evacuation, including several mothers and some men. Among the men were a number aged between 20 and 30 who were eligible to serve in the armed forces. Approximately 17,000 people were evacuated, leaving 23,000 people on the island. In their rush to leave, many people abandoned cattle, horses, poultry and caged birds; dairy cows were left unmilked and there were many casualties among this non-human population. Were it not for the humane actions of farmers who stayed behind, milking the cows and caring for other animals and birds, the casualty rate amongst these hapless creatures would have been considerably higher. The evacuation had a devastating effect on families and former nurse, Barbara Broadbent, tells of how her sister was sent to live in England:

> 'Pam, my younger sister, was just 5 when she evacuated and we never heard anything from her. We were cut off, you see, the mail-boat didn't come so we didn't know where they were taking them. They went on coal boats, cattle boats, any boat. I was jolly glad there was no submarines in the channel that day; we'd have lost a whole generation of children. But we didn't hear for 18 months'.

Midway through the evacuation, and in response to what Jurat Leale called 'the urgency of the hour', a Committee was established in late June 1940 to ensure the maintenance of effective government should Guernsey be drawn into the war. This Committee was to become known as the Controlling Committee of the States of Guernsey and Jurat John Leale became its President.

AIR RAID AT WHITE ROCK

Following the evacuation it was not possible for the island to return completely to normal, but life had to go on. Guernsey's economy depended largely on exporting its agricultural produce and the tomato season was in full swing. The Summer of 1940 was hotter than usual and St Peter Port Harbour, or the 'White Rock' as it was locally known, was experiencing a constant stream of heavily-laden lorries awaiting the transfer of valuable produce for onward shipment to the British mainland. It was on Friday 28th June 1940 that the horrors of war descended out of a cloudless sky, bringing with it death and merciless destruction to unprotected people and their property. In addition to the usual convoy of tomato lorries, the mail-boat was just leaving harbour and the quayside was crowded with people waving off friends and relatives.

Apparently, without warning, five warplanes of the German Luftwaffe appeared from over the sea. Bombs and terrifying machine-gun fire raked the harbour and its jetty, killing or injuring many people, including farmers trapped in their blazing lorries. Blood, mixed with juice from shattered crates of tomatoes spilled across the jetty. People desperately seeking cover were shown no mercy as cannon fire raked the sea front causing devastation that extended beyond the harbour to include surrounding property and the Old Town Church. The raid brought violent death to 34 people, including a well-known policeman, PC 'Chipper' Bougourd. He was giving first aid to the injured when a machine-gun bullet pierced his helmet, killing him instantly. Thirty-three other people were wounded, some seriously. Operating theatres situated at the Country Hospital (later to be renamed the Emergency Hospital), in the Parish of Catel, were stretched to the limit in an effort to treat the wounded, with nursing and medical staff working far beyond the point of exhaustion.

One hundred and eighty bombs were dropped on Guernsey and the neighbouring island of Jersey during that day. Official hospital records stored in the archives of the Priaulx Library, St Peter Port, starkly show 'war operations' as the cause of death for those who did not escape.

A PERSONAL OBSERVATION OF THE AIR RAID

Ossie Gallienne, a St. John Ambulance man at the time, vividly recalls the air raid. Earlier in the day, along with many other islanders, he had attended the Guernsey Evening Press office to hear a speech by HM Procureur, Ambrose Sherwill, who was chairman of the Island's Controlling Committee:

> 'We all trooped up to the Press office, most of his speech was reassurances. Afterwards I went to the ambulance station to let them know what it had been about. When I got to the top of the rise, three German planes came in from the East. They must have flown right over the harbour and in line with the harbour. The first plane suddenly started a trail, a small trail and it went straight to the East. I knew what this meant as I had heard that before they ever started in a new place, started to raid, they would warn their friends to get out of the way'.

Ossie recalls going to the ambulance station and telling people there what he had seen, and that he knew there was to be an air raid. His observations were not believed. One of the ambulance staff remarked that he was mistaken, Ossie was told that the Germans were just reconnoitring as they had done a few days before. He recalls:

> 'Whilst we were arguing, the plane, having turned around, came back from the West, straight along the smoke trail towards the harbour, over the top of the first aid room roof. I could see the plane still approaching the harbour by then, and it dropped a bomb. The bomb went down about a hundred feet or so, and burst open; the main bomb went down surrounded by incendiaries. Then came the explosion, the phone rang and the air raid siren went off. Charlie Froom (an ambulance colleague) took the call and said,

"We've got to go down to the harbour".

I said "do you want me to come down with you?"

"No, you stop here and take the phone calls, Lionel Taylor (another colleague) and me are going down".

'So he jumped in the ambulance and off they went'.

The ambulance was badly damaged by shrapnel and Lionel Taylor was one of many brave men and women who were to receive serious injuries during the raid. Ossie remembers that following treatment and rehabilitation at the Country Hospital:

'The nurses made Lionel stay on.... because his people were away and he remained there more or less for the rest of the Occupation'.

Another brave ambulance driver, Mr Joseph Way, also received injuries from which he subsequently died when his vehicle was riddled with bullets in St James Street.

It transpired that this air raid represented the first action of an impending German Occupation. On Sunday 30th June 1940, a single plane of the German air force landed on Guernsey, the pilot quickly established that no armed resistance was forthcoming. Later that same day a Luftwaffe platoon landed – the Occupation of Guernsey had begun. Guernsey's neighbouring islands suffered a similar fate, with the Union Jack being hauled down from all government buildings, to be replaced with the hated German swastika. German troops were to become fully installed and Guernsey, along with Jersey and Sark, had begun what was to become a long experience of life under the jackboot of German martial law. Alderney was virtually abandoned by its island population and the occupying forces used this most northerly of the Channel Islands to house foreign workers, who laboured under appalling conditions to satisfy the demands of their brutal captors. Whilst it is not our intention to focus on this aspect of the Occupation, we recognise the intense suffering that occurred on Alderney. Interested readers should seek out other texts that explore this human tragedy in depth.

EVOLUTION OF THE EMERGENCY HOSPITAL

On the 15th November 1940, the States of Guernsey Controlling Committee issued a formal mandate designating the Country Hospital to become the Guernsey Emergency Hospital. This hospital was to provide a service for civilian islanders during the Occupation, and also absorb the work of the local Lady Ozanne Maternity Home and a small cottage hospital known as the Victoria Hospital Corporation. The occupying forces were to identify another of the Island's hospitals (now known as Princess Elizabeth Hospital) for their own use. They also used the old Victoria Hospital, but records relating to both these hospitals are not freely available. However, hospital records dated 4th March 1941, show that the management of the Emergency Hospital House Committee had received a telephone communication from the German medical authorities at the Victoria Hospital on 28th February 1941, demanding that a nurse be sent there for duty. There was some reluctance to comply, but as this was a direct order from the 'German Doctor' a nurse was duly sent. Beryl Ozanne recalls that during the early part of the

Occupation, German doctors and surgeons made use of the operating theatres and wards at the Emergency Hospital to treat their own men. This arrangement did not last for long, and once other provision had been identified, it seems that no enemy soldiers were ever again admitted for treatment.

It is important not to confuse these hospitals with the notorious German Underground Hospitals built on Jersey and Guernsey with imported forced labour during the Occupation years. These cold forbidding places were constructed initially for the storage of munitions, but later adopted for the treatment of German military front-line casualties. These days they are maintained as museums, giving a stark reminder of the cruelty metered out to those who were forced into digging the tunnels, many dying in the process.

Managing the newly designated Emergency Hospital was a complex business, becoming the responsibility of two committees, each with a defined function. The Emergency Hospital Committee formed the main governing body, overseeing all that went on in the hospital. This committee had 11 members, each being a person of some influence. It was to be headed by an elected President nominated from among Members of the States of Guernsey, who would remain in office for three years. Six other members to be elected, again from among Members of the States (two to retire annually but remain eligible for re-election). It was considered prudent to have a representatives from the Lady Ozanne Maternity Home, the Victoria Hospital Corporation (neither to be medical practitioners) and local branch of the British Medical Association who would elect the final two members.

A further committee, styled the 'House Committee', had delegated responsibility for the day-to-day running of the service, being charged with drawing up a Book of Rules that would govern all aspects of the hospital's work. This committee was expected to meet on a weekly basis with delegated authority to deal with the following matters:

- Engage and dismiss nurses.

- Purchase all medical stores required and in addition instruments not exceeding £25 per month.

- Examine and pass for payment all accounts due by the Hospital.

- Fix patients' fees and take steps to ensure payment

- Receive written and verbal reports from the Matrons and Hospital Caterer.

- Order necessary repairs, not exceeding £25.

- Make recommendations for purchases, repairs, alterations, or additions exceeding £25.

- Should empty beds be limited, arrange the number of cases to be admitted by each Medical Officer.

- Deal with matters of urgency, make temporary regulations, and report to the President.

- In case of a vacancy in the post of Matron, or Hospital Caterer, advertise, but pending the decision of the latter the House Committee may make temporary arrangements.

- Report at the next meeting of the General Committee all matters of importance or interest.

(Adopted from the States of Guernsey Emergency Hospital Mandate 15th November 1940)

The first elected President of the Emergency Hospital Committee was John Roussel Esq. and Dr. A.N. Symons was elected President of the House Committee. The actual date of transfer of the administration of the Country Hospital (States of Guernsey Emergency Hospital) to The Emergency Hospital Committee was December 1st 1940.

ISLAND PATIENTS

The Mandate required that patients admitted to The Emergency Hospital would be expected to pay for care and treatment. Those unable financially to defray hospital fees and were receiving public assistance at the time of their admission would qualify for 'Island Patient' status. These patients, who would receive special consideration, had their own medical officer, but were not allowed to stay in the hospital for more than six weeks without special permission. They also had to make application for a bed, with each case placed on a waiting list. In cases of urgency the House Committee would decide the order of precedence.

~ II ~

Leadership in the
Emergency Hospital

AMALGAMATING THREE HOSPITALS to form one Emergency Hospital created a nursing hierarchy that included three matrons. Each clinical component of the new hospital had previously employed its own matron, so to save argument a position had to be found for these senior people commensurate with their previous status. This decision effectively created three hospitals in one. The matrons received notification of their responsibilities at a meeting of The Emergency Hospital House Committee held on 24th December 1940. Matron Ella Elizabeth Rabey was appointed to take charge of the medical department. The previous incumbent had been a feisty Sister Stephens who was given the onerous responsibility for hospital catering. We will hear more of Sister Stephens' exploits later.

Matron Ellen Hall was asked to head the surgical department, which included the operating theatres. She would be in charge of the Ward Maids whilst they were actually working in the wards, even though such maids came under the control of the Caterer as regards appointments or discharges. Matron Emily Ruth Finch was appointed to head the maternity department. Her responsibilities also included the children's ward.

(opposite) **Medical Ward D**
Matron Rabey (seated) with patients and staff.

Matrons appointed to the Emergency Hospital were required to meet strict criteria laid down within the Mandate. Each would be single or a widow without the cares of a family, and when appointed should not be under 30 years of age. Matrons were designated as 'Head of Department', holding a three year Certificate of Training gained in a large general hospital, usually a mainland teaching hospital. In addition they would be on the State Register of Great Britain. A matron's salary could vary between £120 and £200 per annum, depending upon seniority. She would be provided with a furnished apartment, firelight, uniform, laundry, and for the most senior matron, the services of a maid. It was a highly prestigious job, carrying immense responsibilities. By the nature of restrictions placed upon them, matrons had to be totally dedicated to their work. They could not be absent from the hospital without leaving a senior nurse in charge; neither could they leave the hospital at night without gaining express permission from the House Committee, or President, or Vice-President in cases of emergency. There existed a requirement for them to maintain standards of care at the highest level possible. This was achieved through personal example and by conducting ward rounds on a regular basis. Matrons had the responsibility for recommending appoint- ments to their respective departments, organising annual leave, ensuring that as far as possible nurses could take time to attend divine service, and arranging opportunities for nurses to take regular outdoor exercise. It was clearly understood that all staff under their jurisdiction carried out orders without question or hesitation. Despite these trappings of power, matrons were under the strict control of the House Committee. They appeared before this body on a weekly basis to give an account of themselves, which included the quality of care given to patients by their nursing and support staff.

Each matron was eminently trained and experienced in the branch of nursing for which she had delegated responsibility. For example, Matron Rabey, who some regarded as the senior of the three, was a native of Guernsey. She was certainly senior in terms of age, being the older by five years. Matron Rabey commenced her training at the London Royal Free Hospital in 1914, where she worked for 25 years, becoming a highly respected ward sister. In 1939, at the age of fifty-seven, she returned to Guernsey to enjoy a well-earned retirement. However, it was not to be, because shortly afterwards she was approached by the President of the Air Raid Precautions Committee of the States of Guernsey who asked her to become Matron of 'The Emergency Hospital' for the duration of the war. Following a strong sense of duty she immediately agreed, taking up the appointment on 1st September 1939. With enormous zeal she immediately set about converting the Country Hospital, which at that time was a mental hospital and Poor Law institution, to meet its new function, which originally was to nurse civilian casualties. What a different world this was from the glamorous London teaching hospital where she had spent all her previous career.

It was not then envisaged that Guernsey would be occupied by enemy troops, or that two other hospitals would join forces with the Country Hospital to provide a more comprehensive service than was originally planned. Former nurses already in-post prior to the Occupation recall their anxiety at the possibility of a German invasion. They attended a meeting at the Victoria Hospital chaired by Dr Montague, a Jewish physician, who reassured them that a German invasion was unlikely and implored the nurses to stay:

'There'd be no danger, the Germans won't come here, a little place like this. What would they come here for?'

The Victoria Hospital and other nursing homes were closed approximately 10 days before the German forces arrived, but the nurses were requested to stay on, which of course they did. In the week following the meeting Dr Montague is reported to have left the Island. The newly designated Emergency Hospital became fully functional on 15th November 1940.

Being a matron in this situation was a high-pressure job. Her principal responsibility was to ensure that staffing and resources were available to meet patients' needs. This responsibility was compounded when attempting to provide a service to people living in conditions that progressively came to resemble those seen in a prison camp. As the Occupation progressed, food with an acceptable nutritious value became infinitely scarce, thus giving rise to diseases associated with malnutrition. Nursing staff suffered in exactly the same way as the rest of the population, several contracting serious illnesses such as dysentery and diphtheria, sometimes with tragic consequences. One such unfortunate person was Nurse Domaille who contracted diphtheria and died on 29th April 1941.

Fuel rations to keep the hospital heated and the stoves alight began to dwindle. The matrons constantly battled against adversity to provide a reasonable level of care to their patients. Hospital records illustrate that time after time the matrons confronted the House Committee with problems that often had no real solution. An example can be seen in the committee minutes dated 19th August 1941, when Matrons Rabey and Finch where left in no doubt of the seriousness of the fuel position. (Matron Hall was unable to attend owing to theatre duties.) The committee President, Dr A.N. Symons, informed the matrons that 'every economy must be made immediately'. This meant that Aga stoves situated in many of the wards would probably be cut off. Any threat to cut off these essential stoves was always met with fierce resistance.

Matron Finch pointed out that the sterilising was done on the Agas, also the heating of milk and other commodities for the patients. The President was adamant, stating that if the conditions became too bad, such work would have to be done on one central stove. At the same meeting Dr Sutcliffe suggested that economies might well be made in the amount of linen sent to the laundry such as towels, sheets and nurses' aprons. He thought that when patients were in for one night only, such as those admitted for dental treatment, then either each sheet could be used again without being laundered, or the patient is put only in a blanket. Further, that in circumstances where sheets are normally changed weekly it might be possible to extend their use for a further week before laundering. Being left with no other option, the two matrons promised to do all they could to make economies in the use of fuel and the amount of soiled linen sent to the laundry. It is not hard to imagine the moral dilemmas faced by the matrons and their staff each time economies such as these were called for.

On a lighter note, the House Committee meeting held on 26th August 1941, heard that Matron Finch, upon requiring the removal of a 'labour case' to the ward, had sent for two male nurses to carry out the task. However, only one male nurse was available and he arrived accompanied by the boilerman to perform the duty. It was not the first time such a situation had arisen and Matron Finch was becoming quite fed up with it. The hospital employed four full-time male nurses (two on permanent night duty) and one part-timer, Male Nurse Clark. The solution to Matron Finch's problem was to 'utilise Clark as a spare male nurse for the surgical and medical wards and that there would always be two male nurses on duty'. Matron Finch seemed satisfied with this arrangement. Much to his relief, the boilerman would no longer be pressed into service.

Matrons also dealt directly with complaints received from patients. For example, on 23rd June 1941, Matron Hall reported that Miss Grace Martell, a patient on 'A' Ward had alleged that 3 pairs of stockings and 1 pair of knickers were missing from a suitcase when this was returned to her on discharge from the hospital. The unlocked case had been stored with others in the lumber-room and because of this the committee would not accept responsibility for the missing items. Dr Fox, a committee member, vouched for the patient's honesty, which then threw suspicion onto hospital staff. Investigations would have been kept 'in-house' but the thief, if indeed one ever existed, was never identified, but this incident raised important questions concerning security of patients' property. In order to avoid any similar incidents the Matrons were asked to introduce a system whereby patients' belongings not immediately required in the ward would be kept under lock and key.

Visiting hours also came under scrutiny. At a meeting of the House Committee held on 4th March 1941, it was decided to reduce the visiting time from two hours on Sundays, Tuesdays and Thursdays, to one and a half hours on the same days. Matron Rabey said she welcomed this decision, as two hours was too long.

One could be excused for thinking that a matron's life was all administration, but not so, as there were often moments of excitement and danger. One such episode is recorded in the Emergency Hospital Committee minutes of 24th November 1943, where it states that the Vice President wished to bring to the notice of the committee the conduct of four members of the Hospital Staff. On the afternoon of the 16th November 1943, an ugly incident occurred at the Hospital when a man in a drunken state entered the building brandishing an open razor, threatening violence to all and sundry. Matron Rabey and Mr Warr, a hospital official, intervened to protect the patients, whilst Mr Cochrane, the Hospital Secretary disarmed the intruder, consequently bringing a dangerous situation under control. The only casualty was the man himself, who received a cut to the right hand. Matron Hall dressed the man's wound, administered a 'good dose of bromide' then put him to bed. The Vice President thought that the conduct of these four staff members was worthy of the Committee's commendation. A letter dated 26th November 1943, was sent to each of them.

It read as follows:

Miss E. Rabey
Matron
Emergency Hospital

Dear Madam,

My Committee and I wish to thank you for your help during the recent disturbance created by a drunken man at the Hospital. Your promptness in taking his razor from the room removed much of the danger.

A commendation is recorded in our minutes.

Yours faithfully,

J. Roussel
President.

Another incident involved a spirited defiance of German orders. On its return from a raid over Germany, a stricken British aircraft had come down in the sea, close to Vason Bay. St. John Ambulance men went to the rescue, taking injured survivors straight to the Emergency Hospital for treatment. This action was in direct contravention to German orders, which required that these men should have been delivered directly into their hands. In the true spirit of their profession, Matron Rabey and her colleagues cared for these airmen, dressed their wounds and provided dry clothing. It was only when they had recovered from their ordeal did the hospital relent, reluctantly handing them over to the German authorities. Expecting the worse, hospital staff awaited some form of recrimination, because after all a serious breach of German orders had occurred. To their relief nothing more was heard of the incident.

Former nurses have many anecdotes about their matrons, some humorous, some serious, some sad, but at all times respectful. One such anecdote involves a game of hockey being played in the nurses' accommodation directly above the quarters occupied by Sister Clayton, one of the senior nurses. The story is as follows:

> 'Oh yes, we were playing hockey in the bedroom above her bedroom one evening, with stockings rolled up into balls and scuttering around. It was quite early you know, before 10 o'clock. Up comes Sister Clayton, sent by the switch(board) to tell us off and report us to Matron Rabey who came along and stood at the door. "You shouldn't disturb people down below, you know", she was grinning all over her face, because she was a dear old girl actually. She thought it was quite funny.'

Rachel Rabey, Matron Rabey's niece, recalls another anecdote for us. When the island was evacuated in June 1940, there was a four-month-old baby girl in the hospital. She was seriously ill and not expected to live so her family evacuated without her. With careful nursing care she regained full health, growing into a dainty little girl. The baby's name was Joyce Kirby and because she had no home it was agreed that she could live in the hospital. Matron Rabey loved this little girl dearly and Joyce became an important part of her life during the bleak war years. Joyce was special, she received a great deal of individual attention from the Matron who dressed her in beautiful hand-made clothes as well as provided footwear from her own limited financial resource.

The purchase of footwear for Joyce eventually came to the attention of the House Committee where it is recorded in the minutes of 17th June 1941 that the Secretary, Mr H.W.

Cochrane, asked whether Matron Rabey could be reimbursed out of the Committee funds. Following debate the President, John Roussel, agreed to take up the matter with a view to a clothing allowance being charged to the evacuation account or some similar fund. In the meantime, the secretary was authorised to defray the cost of one pair of shoes at three shillings and three pence.

When Joyce began to try out her new shoes she would run about, getting under people's feet. After a while it was decided that the hospital was not a suitable place for a child to live so Nurse Helene Duquemin (Duquie to her colleagues) took her home. Helped by her sister and brother-in-law, Eve and Henry Blondel, Joyce was cared for and eventually adopted by the Blondel family. Even in retirement Matron Rabey maintained contact with her, and when recalling events from her own childhood, Rachel Rabey thinks she once met Joyce at her aunt's house, she certainly remembers Matron Rabey talking about her on many occasions. Joyce eventually married, becoming Mrs Elwell, but sadly died in July 1995. Three years later, on 9th July 1998, Duquie also passed away.

We are reminded of Matron Rabey's instincts for nursing in a letter dated 3rd July 1944.

'Dear Matron.

I find it almost impossible to put into words what my wife and I think of your kindness to my mother and us, all the time she was ill. This made it much easier for us to bear knowing what care and attention you gave her and, that she liked having you around.

I don't know how you could spare the time with all your own worries and the endless other work and duties you had to undertake.

We both feel that you might have been a very dear relation, so kind and thoughtful were you at all times.

I thank you Matron from the bottom of my heart and I do hope we meet again under happier circumstances. Perhaps when transport is easier you could come and see us.

I hope some day to thank all your Nurses and Sisters personally. They couldn't have been better.

Yours very sincerely

George Kinnersly.

This letter exemplifies what an important example Matron Rabey was to her junior nurses – they looked up to her. The same observation can also be made about Matrons Hall and Finch. On a daily basis the nurses would witness sensitive, expert and disciplined care being given by these experienced, dedicated women. Even with the passage of so much time there is little wonder they are still vividly remembered with such affection.

THE WARD SISTERS

Working directly beneath the level of matron were the ward sisters. These senior nurses were appointed to respective departments within each general area of care and it was an expectation, although not an absolute requirement, for each to be fully qualified and on the State Register of Great

Britain. One such person was the late Miss M.F. Collas S.R.N. C.M.B. who worked in the surgical department of the hospital. In addition to the nursing and welfare of patients within their wards, Sister Collas and her colleagues had a prescribed list of other duties. These included upholding discipline and conduct, making arrangements for each patient to be visited by a minister of religion, and ensuring the safe keeping and correct administration of drugs or 'poisons', as they were then called. Sister Collas died in January 1998.

Sisters also were responsible for supervising and providing a role model for young unqualified and inexperienced nurses, who, in the absence of any formally controlled training, gained most of their practical skills from observing and generally 'sitting next to Nellie'. The responsibility for supervision and instruction would often be delegated to a staff nurse. Such was the code of discipline, once on duty a Ward Sister could not leave her ward for longer than 5 minutes without informing matron or, in some cases, a more senior ward sister. The nature of nursing in the Emergency Hospital typifies the total dedication to patient care that was the hallmark of this particular era. The process of socialising young nurses into the work was achieved through a well-defined hierarchy of power, control and discipline designed to keep the mind firmly on the job.

~ III ~
Nursing Tales

Nurse Barbara Toms in 1941, showing the nurses uniform of the time.

N OW THAT THE STRUCTURES of the hospital and the
roles of senior staff members have unfolded, it
seems a propitious time to reveal the story of the
people who survived to share their tales with us about nursing
in Guernsey during the Second World War.

In the beginning, like their compatriots on the mainland,
the people of Guernsey thought the war would be short lived;
they had no idea that this world event would last years. Those
who stayed on the island rather than migrating to the
mainland seemed to continue their lives as usual. Even when
the invading German troops arrived there was an air of almost
genteel Occupation. Newsreel footage of the early months of
the Occupation show the Guernsey people going about their
daily lives as the German soldiers walk around the town, for
all the world emulating tourists. It was not too long, however,
before the Islanders began to experience the early effects of
living in an occupied country. Many women found themselves living alone, their husbands often contributing to the
'war effort' as part of the British Forces. This situation
required them to find some way of earning a living.

STARTING OUT IN NURSING

The scarcity of employment, combined with external controls
imposed by the invading force, meant that a number of

women found themselves considering a nursing career. Marge Martel remembers that during the final year of the Occupation she needed to supplement her income to maintain her independence:

'I applied, because I wanted a job. I was already married then. I had my son when I was 21, and this was [now] 1945. My husband was in the navy so I didn't see him for 5 years, he didn't see the baby until he was 5. So, yes, I wanted a job, I applied, and quite enjoyed it too.'

Other women found that their prior employment was forbidden as it could lend itself to accusations of espionage. One such individual was a young woman called Mary Ogier. Her career had until then been in photography; it goes without saying that the taking of public photographs was forbidden, or rather 'verboten'; a word that the people who experienced the Occupation learned to hate. Mary describes her transfer into nursing:

'I lost my job the whole time of the Occupation: once the Germans had landed then photographs weren't allowed to be taken , I was developing films so I lost my job, you see. That's how I came to be on the maternity ward. I had no idea of going into that sort of thing, but I loved it with the babies, I must admit.'

Another found herself in nursing through family connections at a very young age:

'When I came out of grammar school there weren't many jobs at all. As my cousin was nursing already in the hospital, she sort of asked the matron's assistant, her cousin. Then I was over 16 and I thought, well yes, why not, you know, it would be

quite nice really, so that's when I started and joined her up there on the maternity ward.'

Three stories that typify the way young women of that time entered into nursing. Although perhaps not too different from the routes travelled today, two major differences are evident when hearing about their early experience of nursing. These are related to the way that the hospital services were restructured, as outlined in Part One. Firstly, the pressures of working in a compressed environment where three separate hospitals had been merged. Secondly, the tensions created by this merger, meant that communications between the three sections of the hospital could be a little constrained.

The seniority of the three matrons and the resulting separation created between the care areas meant that, although the actual space was small, there was limited interaction between medical, surgical, maternity and children's nursing. Unlike today, new and trainee nurses who worked in each of these separate environments did not rotate between the services to enhance their experience. Rather, they remained dedicated to one area of service. This jealous use of staff limited the extended experience of individual nurses, in particular, those novices who anticipated some form of training. In her forward looking way, Matron Rabey wanted to expose all junior staff to a circuit of training, but the organisation of the hospital did not permit this. As one nurse remembers, for the sake of efficiency, they'd moved everyone to the Emergency Hospital. Matron Finch who was on Maternity moved there, Matron Hall from the Victoria Hospital brought all the surgical work, and the medical wards under Matron Rabey were here already. The segregation made for quite a bit of ill-feeling. There was no mixing of staff, which was a great pity.

So, early in the Occupation the bureaucratic structures that created the Emergency Hospital can be seen to have a major influence in the education and experience of new nursing staff. Set against this, there was the possibility of asking for a transfer between the areas when vacancies arose, Barbara, remembers her transfer from the maternity ward:

> 'When I moved down to the surgical ward, I mean some of the names of the diseases and operations – I thought, oh my God, I'll never learn all that – but I was so glad I'd gone down there – it did help me when I went away to train.'

Ossie, as a man who worked as a volunteer within the hospital and as an attendant on the Ambulance service, found himself in a more privileged position with regard to widening his horizons. He found that his duties took him where he was needed, which meant that he frequently circulated around the ward areas. To today's readers, who are influenced by concepts of equality and view status from position rather than gender, this situation may seem incongruous. However, at the time of the Occupation, the patriarchal role models held greater sway, perhaps, than we acknowledge now. More of Ossie and the role of the male nurse shortly.

So these young women became nurses, at or during the time of the Occupation. They joined others who had transferred from the Victoria Hospital Corporation and the Lady Ozanne Maternity Home. Each one entered this career with the many doubts, fears and excitements typical of new nurses throughout time. In turn, they were to confront challenges and conditions of living and caring that were particular to this relatively short period.

This decade continued the development of the role of women in society, although the social divisions that had been evident in the First World War did appear to be overcome. Dorothy Moriarity provides an example of this in her *Memoirs of a Nurse*, in which she highlights the consternation expressed by her family when announcing her decision to train as a nurse at the beginning of the First World War. She came from a genteel although far from rich family, but her mother regarded her as too frail and too innocent to enter into the world of nursing. She, of course, showed her tenacity and completed her training because she wanted to do something that was of significant value towards the war effort. No such adverse snobbery confronted these nurses on Guernsey, although the divisions between the genders were still evident.

Nursing in this era was a female occupation. The archived documents from the Hospital Committees identify the nursing population as being entirely female, the doctors as being all male. Where they existed, male nurses were seen as a separate nursing division, performing duties suited to their male physique, that is mainly manual tasks. The male nurse provided a useful strong back, some strength in managing difficult and potentially violent patients; he was used in versatile ways from lifting through to floor polishing. 'Real' nursing was performed by women.

Ossie highlights the ways in which the confusion between gender roles and the nursing hierarchy could be rationalised. He elaborates on this through his ability to talk to Matrons as equals on the one hand, yet on the other hand maintain his expected role within the hospital. On one occasion he was concerned about the lack of progress one patient was making and the apparent harm being inflicted by a physiotherapist. He recalls that during a period on the surgical ward there was a patient who was clearly suffering. Following an examination Ossie discovered a shortening of the leg indicative of either a fractured pelvis or a fracture of the neck of the femur. So he confronted Matron Hall,

'Look, this man is being made to walk, he's got a fracture.'

'Oh no,' said Matron, 'I've seen the plates myself and he definitely has no fracture of the femur. The bone is entirely intact.'

Ossie replied, 'there's no fracture of the shaft of the femur, but he hasn't been x-rayed around the area at the top of the thigh, the actual neck of the femur. It's either that or he has a bad fracture of the pelvis.'

He continued ' If I'd picked him up myself in the road, I'd have brought him in as a fractured neck of femur'

Although it was not usually acceptable for junior staff to speak to matrons in such a direct manner, it seemed that because of Ossie's experience in the ambulance service he was the exception. Apparently Matron accepted the argument, informed the doctor of Ossie's thoughts on the matter and sure enough, following an x-ray examination of the injured limb the patient was seen to have a fractured neck of femur.

As an individual he seems to have found a niche that allowed him to develop a dignified position in relation to the demands of the wards for his physical strength and those of his gender. Additionally, as with any environment that combines young women with young men, there were numerous occasions when various pranks helped morale. Although they found many ways to lighten the 'burden' of their toils, the reality of nursing in the Emergency Hospital was a prescribed life of 'all work and no play'. It is not in the nature of young people to forego play, and entering into the occupation of nursing, whether regarded as a vocation or a career, could not remove the humour. Indeed, it seems almost as though the triumph of the spirit over the turmoil of long, strenuous, duty hours was a feature of the survival. An indomitable spirit certainly is evident in the memories of nursing during the Occupation.

'LIGHTENING THE LOAD'

It is well known that all work and no play is an unhealthy tenet. When disciplined regimes are contained within lengthy hours of nursing work, the exuberance of youth will emerge, often in fun claimed at the expense of others. The nature of the pranks usually involved a man, often Ossie it seems, preparing a trick well in advance, usually playing on the fears of the young nurses. Not that they were upset by his jokes, rather they enjoyed them and remember the occasions he spent on their wards with fondness. Two stories in particular highlight the nature of these pranks; both centre on the unsuspecting nurse being given a fright in the dark.

Whilst on night duty Ossie would pin a white sheet against the outside of a maternity ward door. When nurses went through to check on the babies they would walk into this white sheet, startling them. Another trick played on the unsuspecting nurses involved the positioning of an inflated surgical glove, smeared in petroleum jelly or some other greasy substance, across the light switch. He no doubt waited with much delight for the first nurse who needed to turn on that light switch, finding much satisfaction from her suppressed squeals, after all, Sister or Matron must not be alerted to such nefarious goings on. Not that the young men had everything their own way, payback time did come every so often. The nurses recall one such occasion when a number of them organised an attempt to turn the tables on Ossie.

He prided himself that no one could frighten him, so one day – in the surgical ward – the nurses placed a colleague on a stretcher, covered her with a sheet, pretending that she had died. Ossie was called to assist in wheeling the 'corpse' down to the mortuary. Some way along it was planned that an accompanying nurse would stick a pin in her so she'd sit up rather suddenly?

Other nurses hung out of the ward window to watch the scenario unfold. As planned, just as the trolley party reached the mortuary door a pin was produced, the nurse on the stretcher given a hearty jab, making her sit up rather quickly. Covered from head to toe in a white sheet, she must have been quite a sight, particularly as it was so unexpected. To ensure maximum effectiveness the nurses made sure that Ossie had the head part. True to his own boast he didn't turn a hair, the plot had backfired, particularly as the rumpus disturbed Matron Hall whose room was just above the mortuary. She, unlike the nurses, was not amused.

It seems that despite the rigours of night duty the hours could be long and tedious. Some spontaneous joking was essential to maintain the spirits of these young people, to help them continue to deliver care in what were very constrained circumstances. The Doctors were aware of the need to lighten the atmosphere and enjoyed a prank or two themselves, played at the expense of the nursing staff of course. Beryl Ozanne tells this story about a joke played by one of their favourite Doctors – Dr William Burton Fox:

'I remember Dr Bill at a Fancy Dress dance? He came dressed as a Sister in his wife's uniform. This nurse kept coming up to me, 'How are you?' I could not place her. We were well masked, you see. And it wasn't until I'd eliminated the other doctors that I realised it was him. I went up to him and said, 'You so-and-so.'

'It was my laugh that gave it away. He was really enjoying it!'

So the world of nursing begins to open up to us. Young women, sometimes no more than girls, found themselves following in the footsteps of tradition and rallying round to provide caring services for the people of the Island. Noble intentions running through them to the core, but their youthfulness and their essential humanity espoused in both their nursing and their joy in life. Now that we have joined them in their world of nursing let us move on to see how they managed the everyday acts of caring and nursing.

BECOMING A NURSE

We know that some women, then as now, entered into nursing both by a happy chance and also through a deliberate act. But once in nursing, how did they learn to become a nurse? Earlier you read about the creation of the Emergency Hospital and the rule of discipline invested in the three

Matrons. Part of their collective responsibility was to ensure that these young people took on the mantle of nursing in the ways of their predecessors, despite the tensions of supervision by an occupying armed force.

A feature of this mantle was that all applicants for nursing posts at the Emergency Hospital underwent an interview by one of the matrons. Unattached nurses were expected to 'live in' the supervised surroundings of a nurses' home where they would remain under the watchful eye of Matron Finch and Sister Stephens. The nurses' home, prior to the Occupation, had previously functioned as a children's home. It was well situated, offering wonderful views across to the French coast.

This arrangement did not last for long because on 26th July 1941, at very short notice, the German authorities occupied the building and requisitioned its entire contents for use as a military billet. Gun emplacements were to be established adjacent to the building. The closeness of the hospital and sick people had no impact on the placement of this large gun. It is, perhaps, through actions such as these that the inconsistency of bureaucracy comes to the fore. After all, it was the presence of occupying forces that created a need for an Emergency Hospital, inadvertently determining where nursing staff should live, but a later military need took precedence and the nurses were evicted.

This event made it a collective responsibility for the Matrons to secure alternative accommodation for their staff. This was achieved through using two unoccupied bungalows and placing the remaining nurses with local families, each of which had to be approved by the Matrons who would also investigate any reported breach of discipline. The three Matrons continued to act in loco parentis to these young, would-be nurses. They revered the Matrons, were completely overawed by them, and of course, as decades before and after, they walked in fear of Matron's displeasure. Recalling their days as young, untrained girls they still remember the disciplined structure established by the Matrons with fondness. It was, above all, the role modelling offered to them by these charismatic women that encouraged some to consider entering nurse training once the war had run its course.

Such determination to pursue eventual qualification is even more amazing when their work routine is examined. The energies of the young nurses were often sapped by the rigorous and lengthy hours they were required to work. Long days were the order of the time, but no short weeks for these nurses. They worked seven days a week, some of which were classified as 'short days', starting at 7.00 a.m. and finishing at 5.00 p.m. with one day off per month!:

> '...I remember when we first [started] it was 7 till 9 and then later they changed the system and we went half 7 to half 8, with the 2 hours off.'

Another nurse remembered the actual pattern of the working day:

> 'We used to work from 7 in the morning. You had a cup of tea before starting work, then you would have half-an-hour's breakfast break either at 8 o'clock or half past 8, depending which shift. Then lunch-time was half past 12 or 1 o'clock for half an hour...
>
> ...Split shifts were common...

...If you were off in the afternoon, you'd go to the second lunch, which meant you were free from half past one if you didn't want to eat. Then you'd come back at half past 4, having had your tea – or your teatime anyway – then you'd work until half past 8, with a half-hour supper break...

...Night duty started at half past 8...

...They certainly were very long hours.'

Just as the length of these hours were beginning to seem overwhelming, we were given one additional piece of information, 'And then a day off a month'. This last little snippet just added on as though it was completely normal. It should come as no surprise that they experienced extreme tiredness. Nurses from today may well sympathise with the nurse who was so tired when coming off duty for her day off that she slept through the whole of that day:

'Coming off night duty I was so tired I went to bed at home and didn't wake up until half past 3 the next afternoon, so that was a day and three-quarters dead asleep. I didn't even stir to go to the loo or anything. I was so exhausted.'

Recovering from such demanding hours ate into the precious day off:

'Day off a month, gone! And a half day for sleeping was gone. So you had to wait for another month for your next day off.'

We remember ourselves as young nurses, coming off duty from a series of long days and going to bed and waking up mid-afternoon the next day. We can understand the tiredness, but had two days off every week; in retrospect it seems like part-time work compared to the hours demanded in the Emergency Hospital.

The pattern of their day will seem very familiar to many nurses, past and present. The activities of daily living are a constant demand on the skills and patience of nurses. This occupied environment created additional demands on these young women as they sought to provide the care and nurture for their patients that nursing traditions and professional pride demanded. Given the awesome nature of the hours worked, it became evident that stimulating their memories of the nature of nursing work would, first of all, have produced recollections of the endless time seemingly spent 'on duty'. We then moved on to the nature of nursing work, and the ways in which they received their rudimentary training and understanding of nursing.

NURSE TRAINING IN THE EMERGENCY HOSPITAL

The student nurse of today would anticipate that a large part of the work of a nurse in training would take place outside the clinical environment and some aspect of formal teaching would be evident, usually in a university. For example, a typical pattern for the modern student nurse is that each five-day period is divided between practice and education, with shifts limited to seven and a half hours. We already see the differences in the rigour of the work for nurses during the Occupation. As today, so then, the actual hours of duty on the wards were not the end of their responsibilities: they also studied and attended lectures.

When we were regaled with the stories of the lectures and their learning, our initial expectation was that these occurred inside the working day. Imagine our surprise when we found out that lectures were given after working hours from 9.00pm until 10.00pm one evening each week. These lectures were mostly given by one of the Doctors and some aspects of nursing, particularly anatomy, physiology, nutrition and housekeeping, were given by the Matrons. Our respondents remembered different aspects of their learning, not all of them started in nursing during the early days of the Occupation.

The traditional image of the nurse as handmaiden to the doctor emerges as they remember the various lectures given by the medical staff. These lectures were attended after the completion of the long shifts described earlier:

> 'We started at seven o'clock in the morning. That was our day, seven o'clock until half-past eight at night. We got two hours off a day, 10-12 [or] 2-4. Sometimes the medical ward had a lecture afterwards by Dr Fox from nine until ten o'clock. Then we had to write that out in our spare time, whatever you call spare time.'

The detail and immaculate presentation of their notes must stand as testimony to the dedication they showed in learning and preparing themselves for working with the many and varied problems arising in the Emergency Hospital. Throughout the Occupation all types of patients were admitted, many suffering from serious illness or injury, requiring skilled nursing and medical care.

Earlier, we briefly described how the qualified nursing staff accepted responsibility for training the younger, unqualified and inexperienced nursing force that carried the hospital through the dark years of the Occupation. The closed culture of the Emergency Hospital led to a situation where the matrons, taking account of the needs of patients in their respective departments, decided the nature and direction of any training necessary to maintain departmental efficiency. For example, Matron Rabey developed a course containing a series of lectures on anatomy and physiology for medical nursing, based on her London teaching-hospital experience. Matron Rabey would sit in on Doctor Fox's lectures as a means of keeping herself up to date, allowing her to relate clinical theory to her own teaching, both in the lecture room and on the ward. This exemplified the importance placed on the medical nature of hospital training, and the role that doctors played in the preparation of nurses was viewed as essential.

Lecture notes taken in 1940 and 1941 still survive, and illustrate the style of teaching that typified the knowledge basis of nursing as having its emphasis in anatomy and physiology. In the back of one book are notes from a post-mortem that the nurse had attended, no doubt intended to help in her understanding of the body and add to the knowledge gained from lectures. Each nurse remembered drawing bones and muscles, and having to write up their notes after the lectures in 'neat books'. These notebooks were kept with care and presented in immaculate form. Each page carefully titled and dated, with their notes clearly presented in beautiful copperplate writing, with few errors and no blots, as is typical of the penmanship of that time. Matron Rabey, inspected their notes and checked their accuracy, and her initialled comments are interspersed throughout the books.

Barbara Newman's set of books must be an exemplary example, as Matron's comments range from 'very good' to 'excellent'.

Another nurse recalls a more grisly episode linked to their nursing education, in which Dr Fox came into the room to deliver one of his lectures and gave them quite a surprise:

> *'Do you remember the time when Dr Fox came in? I think we'd done the skeleton and we were having muscles, and he came in with a parcel under his arm in newspaper and popped it down in front of the nurse in front and said, "Would you undo that."*
>
> *It was an amputated leg!'*

Shocking, macabre, over the top perhaps, but the doctor was clearly of the opinion that the only effective way for the nurses to learn about the body was to see and handle the real thing. Today's nurses would not have such an unexpected introduction to anatomy and physiology, nor would they be expected to accept such a startling approach. The dark humour evident in this incident is typical of the times; it is perhaps evidence of the nature of the stress that emerges when working under duress. It certainly echoes some of the introductions to subjects presented by Doctors in the 1960s, when the sensitivities of their students did not need to be taken into account. However, the principle memory of this doctor from the 1940s is one of support and gentleness throughout his practice of medicine. They recalled him with affection, in particular, the pleasantness with which he cared for them when they were ill:

'Dr William Burton Fox – he was a lovely man, he was our resident. It was the way he got up in the night every time; he always had a smile on his face. He was never cross, never moaned at all'.

Although formalised lectures were a feature of the early years, they did not continue with the same regularity beyond 1941. This meant that those who were in at the beginning benefited, but others who joined the nursing staff later than 1941 had little lecture-based training – they simply learned from the experience of watching and copying what others did. It is no surprise that the arduous hours for nurses, combined with the poor diet available on the Island, led to a reduction of the formal teaching through lectures and an emphasis on learning by doing. But the need to learn, and for senior nurses to teach and take responsibility for the work of the novice nurse, remained an imperative throughout the five years.

It is a feature of nurse training at this time, that the major part of learning occurs in the wards, and as a consequence of observing, carrying out the task or procedure, and ultimately achieving competence. This pattern remained a feature of nurse training until almost 1990, when the academic rigours of learning were combined with practical skills to emphasise the need for nurses to learn, practice, and reflect on their practice, in order to enhance their knowledge base. Set against these modern ideas is the evidence from Matron Rabey's presence in the lecture room, that any example she or her senior ward staff set would also be informed by the latest understandings transmitted by the medical personnel. So learning from others on the ward could have been haphazard, but it contained a science of its own.

A former nurse recalls an example of this style of learning. She tells of a time when on night duty in the maternity ward, a patient awaiting the birth of her baby had an epileptic seizure:

> 'I had to rush to save her falling off the bed because she could have damaged the baby. I put a spoon on her tongue to hold it and just to hold her until the fit had finished. It's a funny thing, when I think about it now I feel frightened, yet at the time because you're just doing it, you get on with it.'

Although procedures have changed as knowledge moves on, it is the sentiment of learning by doing and, perhaps, even the embryonic expressions of reflection, that is significant in these examples. The fear of interceding to help a patient becomes submerged by the necessity of the action, and the times of observation, discussion and questioning, reap their reward.

Ossie provides a further understanding of learning by doing, and his experiences reflect a more supportive role to the predominantly female nursing staff. He was not on the regular nursing staff, but as a long-time member of the St John Ambulance Brigade spent much time at the hospital helping out. At first, he attended the hospital on Sunday afternoons, gradually increasing to a fortnight, then to a month or six weeks at a time. He worked initially on the surgical ward, but eventually spent more time on the medical ward, gradually developing a useful array of skills and knowledge that was to make him a valuable member of the hospital staff. He tells of gaining operating theatre skills by simply observing the doctors and others during operative procedures:

'Above the lamp there was a mirror. From where I stood I could watch exactly what was happening during the operation. I was very interested in it, so I became more accepted by the doctors, who realised it would be more advantageous to them in the future. Should anything terrible happen I would be able to help in the theatre, so I kept my eyes open'.

The nurses of the Emergency Hospital picked up the skills as they went along, responding to situations as they arose, gradually developing the 'know how' to deal with almost anything that came their way. They became resourceful, knowledgeable and reliable, through being regularly placed in situations that required a cool head and self-discipline. As two former nurses point out:

'Well the staff nurses, Sister and Nurse Hughes, the day nurse would show us how to make beds or how to use a bedpan. You learned how to do different things for the patients. You were told that if it was the first time you'd done a certain job you had to pretend you'd done it a dozen times before, so as not to embarrass the patient.'

This latter sentiment, to safeguard the patient, is an important indicator of the developing professionalism evident in their work. Theirs was a world of backbreaking work dedicated to the provision of a competent and safe nursing service to the people of Guernsey, at a time when the island was a virtual prisoner to the occupying forces. This required a high level of skill, which developed through observation, and 'trial and error' learning. There were few textbooks or other training resources available, so they were fortunate indeed to have had such remarkable role models in the matrons and other senior nursing and medical staff.

A typical example of the nature of learning 'on the job' is provided through the experience of Mary Ogier as a young nurse who had started to gain some skills and, therefore, the trust of senior staff.

> 'I can remember, it must have been night time, a baby was due and I think it was Dr Rose who would be 'phoned to come. As he walked in I was holding the head of the baby. He said, "Continue, nurse." allowing me to pull the baby out.
>
> I would have been frightened on my own, but with him standing there, it was a marvellous experience, really.'

Unlike today, nurses' training was almost entirely task oriented and focused on the medical and surgical needs of the patients. It was about learning on the run and getting the job done, there was no room in their lives for anything else. Former nurses clearly recalled their rudimentary preparation:

> 'They'd show us how to do things. It made me more determined than ever to do my training when I'd done the 5 years here.'

Anyone who has tried to follow instructions on a TV cookery programme will be aware of the gaps in knowledge and practice that can remain, even after careful scrutiny of the expert's actions. Imagine learning to carry out a procedure that fills many people with alarm – the giving of an injection. As equipment was scarce and certainly could be replaced only with great difficulty this process had to be managed with care and, as we will see, some fortitude:

> 'I had to watch Sister giving injections, and in the end I had to give them myself'.

It is not always easy to see the minutiae of each action and, in particular, to emulate such actions with the skill of the one observed. Hence the need to combine observation with safe practice for some of the more painful tasks, such as the giving of injections. Even when the usual strategies of the time for practising, such as using a piece of fruit, were not available due to rationing, the patient's comfort and safety still required that the novice nurse practice the skill:

> 'I can remember when we had to start giving patients injections. We had to practise on ourselves, with sterile water – we had no oranges or anything like that... By golly it didn't half hurt!'

Today, learning through new situations and as an emergency measure seems fraught with problems, but here we have people recalling the value of such learning and the feeling of success when they achieved complex actions. The senior staff were also prominent in ensuring that the education and training of this new group of nurses was successful. The nurses from our interview groups were always positive about the people they worked with and remembered their mentors with happiness and respect, although a special place of awe always seemed to be given to the Matrons.

~ IV ~

Professional Pride
in Adversity

S O NOW WE HAVE FOUND OUT how these young women came into nursing and why, it is pertinent to move briefly to their feelings – and those of the Islanders about the role and status of nursing during the Occupation. The Island is, and should be, proud of the work and standards of the nurses during this demanding time of war and Occupation. As we have found out, there were many reasons for entering nursing other than the vocational, which is the traditional image of this profession. However, once into the uniform and practice of nursing the ethos of the responsible and accountable nurse became paramount. Despite the exhausting hours and the many privations, both at the personal level and in the lives of their patients, the feelings of pleasure and a 'good job well done' were bright points throughout our discussions. Their thoughts on the way that nursing was perceived during that time show that this profession was highly regarded by the people of Guernsey:

'Oh I think people looked up to you, that you were doing something worthwhile'

'...and you felt quite proud to be a nurse...'

'...I was. I was pleased to have that experience.'

'So was I. I quite enjoyed it, and I'm pleased I did it. I would do it again, actually.'

'You can't forget those years.'

There are many ways in which individual people can maintain their own integrity and spirit in adverse conditions. These nurses found a wide range of strategies for dealing with the rigours of the hours and the nature of their work. In hearing about the length of their working day and indeed of their working month, and knowing the nature of nursing work as being exhausting, it is interesting to explore the ways in which their commitment and humanity were maintained. Pre-eminent in the memories of these wartime nurses are a sense of camaraderie and an unfailing sense of youthful exuberance that forever sought ways to defeat the ogres of exhaustion and war.

When asked about the nature of nursing the tales were of bed-making, dressings, medicine and doctors' rounds, and caring for individual patients as would be expected at any time in the history of modern nursing. The management of these events is of particular interest as this was a unique time in their history and a period of uncommon deprivation. First of all, we will consider the management of nursing time and the support mechanisms for maintaining their physical and spiritual well-being. Their memories are of helping each other stay awake and learning the ropes as they went about their duties, including who could be depended on to let them have an easier time. They supported each other, recognising that they needed to be a team if they were to survive; not so different from the realities of surviving nurse training today, at least at the level of the individual student nurse.

NIGHT DUTY

Anyone who has worked a night shift will recognise the tensions between being worked off your feet and the night flying by leaving you exhausted, and the slow shift that takes an eternity to pass, leaving you just as tired, often unable to keep your eyes open. On the slow nights your shift companions can make or break your morale. Here is one account of how it felt to be working through a 'slow' night:

> 'Well... there was three of us, because there was Nurse Miller and you and I.'

> 'But I know I couldn't stay awake...'

> '2 o'clock was the worst time...'

> 'But with Nurse Miller we had to keep awake... She used to poke us all the time. We had to keep going with Nurse Miller. She'd find us something to do.

> 'Because we used to make swabs, didn't we? She got us making those.'

> 'So if you were busy, it was fine really.'

During these significant years, there was internal rotation to night duty, although not quite as it is experienced today. Rather, the allocation of the individual nurse to nights was for a minimum period of one month, that is, from the end of your day off to the beginning of your next day off, 30 or 31 days and nights later.

> 'I remember being on night duty for much longer than I should have been and Dr Fox telling Matron to take me off before I collapsed. But you just got pale, I suppose. Yes, I think at times, when you went down you really went down.'

Such a comment emphasises the rigorous nature and heavy demands of the work required of young women then. Additionally, these women were existing on a poor diet and under the emotional stresses that accompany any experiences of living in an occupied country where those in control overtly carried rifles. We know that the hospital was divided into three main areas – midwifery and children, medical, and surgical, – each with its own set of staff. The care that is required in each of these areas is both singular and common to each.

NURSING WORK

Many images of the nature of nursing work emerge from the transcripts of the interviews. As you may remember, each nurse had worked during the war years in the very different areas of midwifery, children, medical, and surgical care, with little communication between these wards. Some differences did emerge, but in the main, the nature of nursing in their accounts emphasises the essentials of caring for people, and can be seen through the experience of any of the nurses.

A *typical day*

Trying to map out a typical day was a major tax on the memory. A situation that should give no surprise, since it is the outstanding memories that stay with us, the humdrum everyday events of life pass by, often without seeming to be noticed.

Once they started out on the path to remembering, many aspects flooded back into vivid relief, others remained unclear. The big issue that emerged was that their work was very 'task oriented'. They remembered their roles through the tasks that they were given, and the sequencing of those tasks was determined by the nature of the ward they worked on. For example, in midwifery, the first job for the young nurses was to bathe the babies, whereas in medicine and surgery it was bed-making.

A typical day was made up of a round of tasks, centering on what is today called 'basic nursing care'. These duties included, toileting, bathing, bed-making, the 'back round', delivering trays of food and drinks, and assisting sister with the administration of medicines.

The main early duties centred on helping patients with their toilet and making the beds. They were then allocated individual duties. In the nursery, they had the pleasure of bathing the babies and then of showing the mothers how to manage their tiny new-borns in the bath. At that time, mothers were required to remain in bed for ten days after the birth of their baby:

'*So you had to more or less learn to walk again.*

Ten days and then you were allowed to go into the nursery to be shown how to bath the baby, then a few days later you were allowed home'.

Helping new mothers to breast-feed was an important part of their work, but for some new mums it was not possible, either because of individual reluctance or due to a physiological problem that inhibited their ability to feed their baby. Added to these duties was the need to ensure that where babies were fed with powdered milk, called Klim, that the bottles used were properly sterilised.

Sterilising was also a feature of work on surgical and medical wards, perhaps playing an even greater part in these areas. The boiling of metal instruments in bright metal sterilisers is only part of the task. Each area of the sluice had to be cleaned and left sparkling and tidy:

'Sister usually did the doctor's rounds, and we'd make ourselves scarce then, wouldn't we?'

'Yes, we were the underdogs then, weren't we?'

The disappearance of junior nursing staff when the ward rounds took place did not in any way imply a reduction in their workload. Indeed, in many ways, their strategies for making themselves scarce featured work outside the immediate vicinity of the ward and took them into the sluice-room:

'We had to go and clean all the bedpans, scour them.'

'And the bathrooms – we had to clean the bath. There was always some cleaning up to do.'

'Scrubbing the enamels – we'd have to put them in for sterilising.'

The work ethic influenced even the way in which they 'made themselves scarce'. This involved finding discreet work rather than doing no work:

'We'd go and hide in the nursery if there was anybody we didn't want to see'.

Although this is evidently more pleasurable work than that described when using the sluice for remaining out of sight of the senior round.

Pressure Sores

The main heavy work beyond the sterilising and cleaning centred on the management and avoidance of pressure sores:

' We used to have a 'back-tray', as we called it, with soap and a bowl of water. You put the soap on your hand, rub it on the backside, dry it off without rinsing it with a towel, then you rubbed the skin with methylated spirits and powdered it. That kept everybody fit. It was a terrible disgrace to have a bedsore. You just didn't let anybody have a bedsore ever.'

There were many theories for ensuring that patients who were in bed for extended periods of time did not develop bedsores, and these were often determined by the favourite applications of the nurse in charge. One issue remained constant and that was the ignominy of owning to a patient in your care who had sustained a pressure sore. The regular turning of people and the continuous management of bedding so that nobody lay upon wrinkled sheets contributed to the workload and to the limited breakdown of skin recorded over this time:

'We didn't let the covers be creased at all, or anything. There was really meticulous care about all those things, because to have bedsores, well that was just the end.'

We wondered, particularly in the later years of the Occupation, if malnutrition contributed to the potential for skin to break down. The resounding response was that the intensive nursing care, even during the final years, ensured that what help could be given to a patient was given. So, although standard nutritious fare had been replaced with a more inventive diet, the 'hands on' aspects of nursing were, if anything more vigorously pursued. As this response to the question about poor diet demonstrates:

'Well it didn't, because it was automatic that you did the back round. In fact, I can't remember how many times a day...Because with long-term people, we might have them in for 5 or 6 weeks or more.'

The absence of bedsores is seen as a badge of merit, and it is impressive that in a time when caring was labour intensive, with little technological help, that healthy skin was a feature of the care received in the Emergency Hospital. In particular, if a patient entered the hospital with good skin then they should leave the hospital in improved health, rather than reduced health, therefore no bedsores should develop if good nursing care is provided. Perhaps such a firmly held view is an early echo of the moral position that the hospital should do the patient no harm.

It was not only in relation to medical needs that the Matrons and sisters provided role models and education. The deportment of the individual nurse was also defined. They described themselves as living in a highly disciplined environment. When asked to explain further they gave the following example:

> 'Well the matrons and the sisters were very strict. I mean, we were never allowed to talk to one another on the ward. We had to keep busy all the time, we couldn't be idle, could we?'

Further examples came from descriptions of the demands made on each nurse for their excellence of posture. It seems that each task not only had a clearly defined procedure, but also had to be carried out from set positions. One nurse remembers her sister's favourite story of being corrected about her posture:

> 'My sister was cleaning out the bottom of a cupboard and Sister came out, she was kneeling to get to it. The Sister said, 'Nurses don't kneel, they stoop.' She had to get up and just bend down.'

Perhaps when faced with Matron and the Sisters, German soldiers, irrespective of their rifles, were less frightening than they may have been to anyone without the experience of Matron, who could see through walls, or Sisters who could demand specific standards for posture.

In the presence of a rifle

The privations of these times could easily overshadow the difficulties of living through a military Occupation, particularly of an isolated Island. Although the Liberation of the Island was many decades behind them, the feelings of being restrained and controlled remained very real. Indeed, the nature of the Islanders' interaction with the German soldiers is complex. Nursing work had to be managed under the supervision of military personnel who were highly suspicious of the work being carried out in the hospital. A sense of quiet resistance is felt when reading or listening to accounts of the Occupation. It is not advisable to openly contest an interloper carrying a rifle, but quiet resistance from a disciplined force of workers could be quite effective.

In the first six months of the war, the change in life experiences was quite devastating from both the professional and personal viewpoint. The German soldiers treated any admissions to the wards, particularly at night, as suspicious events. At this early stage of the Occupation, maternity patients were still admitted directly from home when they went into labour. On one such occasion, the escorting soldier felt that he was being hoodwinked when he was required to remain outside the delivery suite, despite the baby having been born:

> 'In 1940 there was a patient in the labour ward and she was delivered of a daughter. There was a German soldier outside the labour ward with his gun at the ready. Unfortunately Matron had to come and tell him that there was another one, another baby coming, that it was going to be a twin delivery. The soldier was furious. He demanded to go in, and he stood in the labour ward to watch this second baby being delivered, because he thought we were trying to hide something, or having another patient coming in.'

The suspicion that the closed door of the labour ward meant that hospital staff were breaking the rules is made clear in this passage. The occupying forces were used to claiming access to any area – no one closed doors on them. Interestingly, this feeling of hostility and suspicion had become the norm after only six months. You may remember that the early weeks of the Occupation were characterised by a friendly holiday-style approach, and it was only as the months continued that the hostility between the groups became more evident. So any admissions, particularly in darkness were treated with great suspicion:

> 'They didn't know what to expect. I mean, they didn't trust anybody.'

> 'It was a shut door and they had no idea what was going on.'

> 'You'd have to have lived through this to be able to appreciate how they thought. He really thought we were trying to hoodwink him and trying to hide something.'

A further difficulty for the nurses and doctors was the protection of their patients, especially if the German soldiers felt that they had somehow contravened the regulations. If any Islander was admitted to the hospital then the staff felt duty-bound to ensure that they stayed until well. This was particularly evident where any individual who had displeased the occupying forces was concerned:

> '...but if anybody was sentenced to hard labour, or anything like that, and became ill, they came into the hospital.'

> 'I remember we had one or two patients who worked for the Germans. Sometimes the Germans would come in to find out how they were getting on because they wanted them back. We were told to tell them they weren't so well and that they had

complications, to keep them in as long as possible. I remember a man in E Ward and I was there when they came in to ask about him. We always told them, 'Well, he's not so well.'

In such seemingly small ways each nurse played a part in resisting the insidious nature of the Occupation. They also internalised the role of caring for people, a most significant role undertaken by nurses, both then and now.

Other strategies that each Islander used to confound the German restrictions was keeping in touch with the outside world. The main recourse here was the use of 'cats' whisker' radios, which were of course forbidden. The official news channels were bulletins in the newspaper and on the newsreel at the cinema, both carefully edited and censured prior to circulation. The cats' whisker radio, on the other hand, was a true link to the outside world. Nurses and doctors were also interested in finding out the true events of the war and found strategies for contravening the restrictions imposed. In this, they were no less resourceful than in overcoming the deprivations of heat, light and food.

'Sister Mansell had a radio because she used to teach the children different songs. Do you remember? So we knew she had a radio somewhere and she always knew what was going on, and she always passed the news on.'

'Dr Rose had one in a clock.'

'I was going to say, one of the doctors had a radio, because in theatre we used to get all the snippets, you know. That was one place you could discuss all the news.'

There are many examples of the ways in which the Guernsey people managed the Occupation years and strove to retain or gain some control over their lives. Many of the examples stem from 'getting one over' on the military. These move from tales of taking butter from the German table if working directly for them, to stealing tins from lorries. More extreme measures were reported to us, such as a pig being passed from farm to farm to avoid enemy censure resulting from the illegal slaughter of pigs for food. So there was a quiet resistance to the occupying forces imposition of petty rules and over strict bureaucracy.

At times it became unclear if the relationship between the occupying forces and the islanders was benign. This was not a true image. On reading and listening to the recordings of our interviews, it became evident that there was and continues to be a bitter resentment over those five years. Perhaps the stories told as to how 'stupid' the German soldiers were exemplify these feelings of bitterness over the experience of being restrained in your own homes and land, without any of the freedoms that are associated with being 'at home'. Such tales are told frequently and can be found in many books about the war. For example, the commandeering of homes was told to us in the following way:

> 'They were quite funny. I remember when they first came to the island, they wanted property. That's how the Victoria Hospital was taken over by the Germans in Queen's Road. This officer, who thought he knew a lot of English, was the billeting officer, 'I will take Autumn Lodge, Victoria Lodge,' so and so, 'and Please shut the Gate.' He thought the label 'Please shut the Gate' was the name of a house.'

'*But they were humourless. They took everything literally, didn't they?*'

The need to reassert their own integrity and authority is established through such stories. Although the pig and 'please shut the gate' tales can be read in a number of accounts, there is a story that seems to be different, as told by one nurse. She tells of her father cycling to or from work during the day and coming across a group of soldiers engaged in a camouflage enterprise at the airport:

> '*This just shows you how humourless they were... He [father] had to stop because there was a German officer walking backwards looking at the hangars that had just been painted. He said to my father, 'Good, yes?', and my father said, 'Yes, very good.' So he said – because it was mostly grass in those days – 'The hangars are the colour of the grass.' My father said, 'Yes, exactly the same colour as the grass.' So he said, 'RAF not see.' And my father said, 'Oh yes they will.' 'Vy?' 'Because there are daisies in the grass, but there are no daisies on the hangars!' The next day when he was cycling ... they were putting little white dots on! I mean, you couldn't see daisies from the air anyway, could you? They were so stupid.*'

Again, the tension between the occupying forces and the Islanders is evident in this extract. The need to supervise every aspect of human life and maintain control of the activity of the whole of the Island meant that the nurses came across armed soldiers both when they were 'on duty' and during their leisure hours. This contact began with the admission of the air-raid victims at the start of the Occupation and continued until Liberation. Even the exuberance of young German soldiers at such times as New Year could have negative consequences, as they used their pistols to 'shoot in' the New Year, causing unwitting injury and in one instance the death of an Islander. Although the German soldiers expressed remorse for this action, it nevertheless created another layer of division in the relationships between the groups that has lasted over half a century. As one nurse put it earlier:

> 'You'd have to have lived through this to be able to appreciate how they thought.'

Heavy workers

Without the additional deprivations of diet, the workload and hours alone must seem excessively onerous to both lay people and nurses. As such, it would seem unsurprising that when special consideration was being made for those who fell into the category of 'heavy worker' that nurses would expect to be included. However, the definition of 'heavy worker' was to be processed through the masculine and paternalistic norms of the time. As the tale of the 'heavy worker' unfolds, hold the nurses working hours in your mind.

As the Occupation progressed bread became scarce and was rationed in much the same way as other commodities. Former nurses remember the small 'Tommy loaves' that represented their weekly ration. Each loaf was cut into three parts and shared out, and if luck was on your side you would be given a slightly larger section, but usually the ration amounted to 'two longish slices and a crust that would have to last for two or three days'. It was the nurse's responsibility to collect patients' food from the kitchen, which in some cases meant quite a long walk. For example, from D ward (situated at the top of the building) there was a trek down three or four flights of stairs to the kitchen (situated at the other side of the hospital) and back again, carrying large plates of food. On the way down the nurses would peek into the dining room to see if the table was laid. If it was not laid then there would be no lunch. They had to rely on their meagre bread ration to see them through to the next meal.

A system of bread rationing for workers was introduced that placed certain categories of labour in a 'heavy worker' category. People classified as 'heavy workers' would be allowed more bread than those who were in sedentary employment. Nurses at the Emergency Hospital were under the impression that 'heavy worker' status should apply to them and as such would become entitled to extra bread. A case was made to the Island Controlling Committee, but this was unsuccessful. A letter to the House Committee dated 19th April 1941 from Sir Abraham Laine, Vice President of the Controlling Committee, stated that the members were unable to place the nurses in the category of 'heavy workers' for the purpose of bread rationing.

Dr Sutcliffe was outraged by this decision and suggested that in his opinion if a nurse is not a 'heavy worker' then nobody is, and the extra ration should not be given to **any** female. Dr Sutcliffe held the view that the feeding of the Island population should be a medical concern, but apparently the doctors had not been consulted and he asked for a formal ruling on what category of female workers were classed as performing 'heavy work'. This was probably a reference to the 'ladies of leisure' imported to keep the

German troops happy. In his book *The Silent War*, Frank Falla writes:

> *'...like all civilian men doing manual work these women were given what was known as 'heavy workers' rations – just a little bit extra compared with ordinary people in sedentary occupations'.*

Falla wryly suggests that it all depends on one's interpretation of 'heavy work'. It is not recorded whether Dr Sutcliffe ever received a ruling on the definition of a female 'heavy worker'.

A similar request was again placed before the Island's Controlling Committee on 10th November 1942, but to no avail. On this occasion it was Dr Symons, in his capacity as a member of the Controlling Committee, who made a request that members of the nursing profession be allowed increased rations, especially bread. He made the point that many of the nurses were young women aged between 18 to 20 years, an age when adequate nourishment was essential, and they were now putting in long hours of hard, exacting work on an inadequate diet. It was Sir Abraham Laine who once again said he could not support this request. He took the view that if additional rations were granted to nurses then there would be other deserving categories of workers who could claim similar treatment. These workers, like the nurses, were precluded from receiving additional rations because they did not appear on the list of 'heavy workers' issued by the French Intendant and approved by the German authorities. Dr Symons could not agree with this ruling and proposed that the matter be raised with the German authorities or the Intendant. The Controlling Committee resolved not to support his proposed action, and there the matter was finally laid to rest.

Lay understandings of nursing work as that of women's work, belied the physically strenuous nature of caring. Indeed, the confusion between the gentler sex and the roles required that women undertake in everyday life are a known paradox. In the examples of nurses working long days, followed by internal rotation on to night shift with very few days off, it does seem that definitions of heavy work are somewhat limited.

Angels

Yet, despite the set back of poor provisions, they endeavoured to live up to the principles of nursing as communicated by their mentors, the Matrons, and knew the extent of their duty to their patients. As at any time, some figures emerge as exemplars of the traditions that others strive to achieve.

One of the group, Mary Ogier, was always referred to as being an exceptional nurse, representing the angelic aspects of nursing, and was always likely to help the struggling novice. On the maternity ward in particular, the night shift could pass slowly and it was the interventions of a friendly senior who could make life tolerable. One image brought to mind was that of a very new nurse experiencing her first nights on duty, who recalled:

> 'Well if I was on with Mary, she'd do all the work. She'd say, 'Stick your head out of the window', 'Wash your face', 'Go for a walk', 'Do something!'-We'd go to the nursery now and then

... but apart from that, unless we had a case in the middle of the night, there was nothing to do.'

Mary worked with some of the others principally in maternity care and she recalls some interesting observations from her early experiences. These are particularly fascinating when trying to uncover the nature of nursing during these trying times.

One of the first necessities to disappear on the Island soon after the Occupation was electricity, which was rationed early on to husband the stores of fuel. Of course, this would make nursing on night duty particularly difficult; many variations of the lamp were soon developed. It is not surprising that carrying a lamp had an impact on impressionable young women:

> *'Talking about the lamps, because at night time we had to have lamps: there was only electricity in the labour ward. I can remember the St John Ambulance Brigade were going to deliver a patient, come up the side stairs, right to the top, to the maternity ward, with a stretcher. I walked out to the top of the stairs with my lamp, and to hold it up so they could see where they were going, and I felt like Florence Nightingale.'*

*'Well you **were** Florence Nightingale!'*

That last comment was made with some depth of feeling, perhaps from the nurse she had supported on those long stretches of night duty.

Hostile lights

There were other sources of light in the dark, although far from welcome. As described earlier, a heavy anti-aircraft gun, used by the German soldiers to fire at anything that flew overhead, was positioned only a short distance behind the Emergency Hospital. When this gun was in use, not only was there a deafening noise, but the flash as it fired was used by the nurses to help them see as they went about their duties. They became adept at using the illumination from this hostile force to maintain their commitment to caring for their patients. Beryl Ozanne recounts the time when she was to administer an injection of morphine, and it was the gun flash that gave her a good view of the patient.

The light emitted from the gun may have had some benefit, but there were many difficulties as a consequence of this hostile use of heavy artillery in the locality of a hospital. Not least was the impact of the noise and sudden light flashes on the unfortunates who were being nursed on the open verandas. The compression of three hospital units into one, in conjunction with the long admissions normal for that time, must have created some crowding on the wards. Certainly, the nurses spoke of having three rows of beds down the long wards, which must have created a fair degree of congestion. So all available space was used, including the verandas, which were open to the elements. They did have heavy tarpaulins ready to pull down if inclement weather or angry gunfire intruded. Nonetheless, the battering of regular gunfire added to the workload of the nurses who often had to comfort and soothe the terrified patients when heavy artillery opened up on over-flying allied aircraft, seemingly from the bottom of their beds.

Personal fears of bombardment were put to one side as nurses recognised the helplessness of those patients on the verandas during such onslaughts. Although they could do little to alleviate the feelings of vulnerability to stray ammunition, they could, and did share the experience with the patients and remain with them to help soothe their distress. The volume of noise as well as the searing flash of the gun must have been overwhelming for both nurses and patients. It is amazing that these nurses accepted this situation as normal, to be expected, and took it in their stride as though it was the most natural thing in the world for nurses to do. A sure measure of the extent to which living in an occupied country can so easily become an accepted and almost familiar part of everyday life. It seems that the role of the nurse as protector enabled them to plumb personal depths of spirit which, until that moment of crisis, had remained hidden and now helped to sustain each one as shells whistled overhead.

~ V ~

Working Hard
but Playing Hard

T HE IMMENSITY OF THE TASK of caring for people under restricted conditions could overwhelm some of the lighter times experienced, particularly 'off duty'. These nurses were young and full of the *joie de vivre* evident in any group of that age. They took their responsibilities seriously, but given the opportunity they also desired to 'live a little'. To our ears, given the nature of the working day, week and month, it came as a surprise that any energy was left for fun and games, but as shown earlier, these young women exhibited an indomitable spirit that would show through even in the worst of times. They remembered many events and occasions that had them laughing, even today, at the pleasures they managed to steal in such adverse times.

CONCERTS

In-house entertainment was a feature of the 1940's and, indeed, continues into the present with revues and sometimes pantomimes. At a time when few new people could join the teams the recognition of talent was essential. Whether an individual had an innate gift for music, or for mimicry, they were co-opted into the concert party. It does seem from the stories told that they were blessed with a good range of talented musicians and singers.

Almost every month there would be a home-grown concert that featured both the excellence of serious and comical talents. Everyone, whatever their position, was called on to contribute:

'They were jolly good, weren't they? The doctors used to take part. One doctor used to play violin, and Dr Rose and Dr Sutcliffe were absolute idiots, you know.'

'They were good, very good, those two.'

They had pianists who played classical music and operatic-style singers who provided a balance to the high spirits and perhaps extreme humour of the younger, more boisterous, groups. Anyone who has taken part in a hospital or village revue will know the surprises that can emerge when harvesting the talent of the few. In this isolated Island, and indeed within the Emergency Hospital itself, there seems to have been quite a range of skills prepared to provide entertainment. Some images that were evoked from our conversations did not sit naturally with the serious and respectable demeanour of our group of past nurses:

'I remember doing an imitation ballet dance with staff nurse wearing a pair of Grecian slippers and a crepe paper skirt.'

The entertainment was not just for the staff, and to use up high spirits and youthful energy the patients were also in need of some respite from the monotony of life and the frugality of lifestyle. When required to stay in bed for lengthy periods of time either because of the restrictive conditions, or to receive the increased nutrition available as an in-patient, recovery time would move very slowly. This was particularly so for post-surgery patients, such as those recuperating from hernia operations who were obliged to lie still and do nothing, not even feed themselves, for several weeks in some cases. Concerts could also be put on in the wards:

> 'We did a concert on B Ward, the male ward. The beds were all crowded in, they couldn't all fit in. We did a silly one-act play called 'The Bathroom Door', and Lionel Turner said to me, 'Have a stiffener before you start.' And he gave us a neat brandy. There were 3 doors, and I didn't know which door I was supposed to be in and out of.'

No one was quite sure where the brandy came from, but it obviously helped the show go on! Christmas was made special through the concerts, and the long winter nights endured through the companionship of friends and colleagues as the next show was planned and rehearsed. The expert violinists, pianists, dancers and singers, are remembered with great fondness. There were sad memories of those whose names escaped them at that time or who were no longer alive, amongst them Theresa Steiner, who had also played the piano for the concerts prior to her deportation. Her story is told later in the book.

PARTIES AND DANCES

Parties and dances put on for the young of the Island continue the theme of self made entertainment. Young nurses, despite working long hours, were not about to hold their social lives in abeyance for the mere sake of being occupied by enemy forces. Rather they would seek ways to circumvent the regulations imposed that curtailed their freedom. Going to a party that could not start until close to curfew due to working hours could make the purpose of the party a pointless exercise, but youth will find a way. In this case, despite the normal values of the time, the only way to have a successful party was to invite your guests to stay overnight. All night parties became the rage and, perhaps to some, an outrage; however innocent the intentions of the participants, the notion of being out all night was adventurous for that period. Family parties would start at 6.00p.m and be finished by 8.30p.m so that the curfew was not broken. The demands of youth, however, were not so modest:

> 'We used to go dancing every Saturday night for a year or two. We came off duty at half past 8, go upstairs, change and cycle out there, get inside the barrier before 9 o'clock. The Germans put a barrier across one of the lanes – the curfew was 10 o'clock and you had to be inside this barrier by 9. Then we'd go to an all-night party and dance all night. Music was provided by an accordion or two, with a car battery for a light – a little bulb. It was marvellous whilst you were dancing, but when you got back in the morning, you had 'toothache in your legs' – it was terrible. You could go to bed and rest for an hour or two before going on duty. If you were off in the morning it was fine, but if you were off at 2 it was agony.'

Anyone who has been hungover for work after a really good night out will know the sentiment expressed in the notion of 'toothache in your legs', especially if you have to be on your feet all day. The regulation of these events was not all in the hands of the German officials. Both Matrons and Sisters frowned upon them, and indeed some of the nurses themselves were uncertain as to the morality of these events, the innocence of the activities notwithstanding.

Two further issues are worth thinking about when reviewing the nurses' leisure pursuits. Firstly, what to wear and secondly, how to get there. As the years wore on and clothing became scarce as no new fabric or garments entered the Island, the recycling of clothes became a major pastime. For some, their grandmother's clothes chest was a veritable goldmine, although here it was more the robust items needed for everyday wear that found this as the source. The necessary fashions for a party or dance were more difficult to come by. For some, dresses were borrowed from families whose daughters or sisters had evacuated before the war. Others made up dresses from several old or outgrown ones. Certainly, any notion of latest fashions was not only difficult to keep up with, but also remained unknown due to the lack of open communication. Nevertheless, they managed to provide themselves with elegant eveningwear when the occasion demanded. The energy toll seemed excessive, but they were determined to enjoy life:

> 'I think it was the work – always running about – on the move the whole time. When I left the hospital, I'd cycle home to St Sampson in my 2 hours off duty, go home and back again. I would come off duty at half past 8, you'd go down to l'Ancresse to dance – and have to be back for 10. I think the exercise, cycling must have done us good or something.'

It seems that an hour of dancing was worth the effort, despite the strict curfew. From the example above this was a summer event as the winter curfew was nine o'clock. The use of a bicycle to journey to social events provides insight as to how they got there. There was very little fuel and certainly none available for frivolous pursuits such as parties or dances. The bicycle was the main vehicle for all. There were many memories of adventures on their bicycles, but not quite what we would expect. The main issue that provided tales of these days was the use of lights and the renewal of tyres.

In Guernsey today, travelling by bicycle is a holiday pursuit enjoyed by many, therefore, perhaps we can be forgiven as seeing this mode of transport through rose-coloured glasses, as we envisage travelling country lanes in sunshine and without any reason to hurry. This is not quite the experience shared by our young nurses, particularly in winter. First, there is the problem of lighting your way in the dark through unlit lanes, and second, the state of disrepair that cycles came to be in by the final years of the war. As you will have read earlier, the recycling of jars and candles for lights was a feature of life on the Island. Jam jars packed with earth, and using a small candle or nightlight suspended by cord from the handlebars, provided the only means of lighting available to the majority of nurses.

The combination of poor wheels using recycled tyres, hose-pipes or even unforgiving wooden replacements, could make journeying to a party rather more of an adventure than is pleasant. There were many fond remembrances of the hose-pipe tyres that bumped along, although we are sure that this is one instance where the gap in time softens the impact of those hard unforgiving tyres!

'Oh yes, it was hose-pipe that I had on mine. I travelled miles.'

'I know. It didn't half bump though.'

'But we got used to it.'

The problem of lights was partially solved by black-out regulations. The dim light afforded by a candle in a jar was the only feasible means of illumination when blackout conditions prevailed. A jam jar dangling from your handlebars was surely more of a comfort light than good illumination. Additionally, it was a fairly precarious source of light that could have its disadvantages. Nurses ventured out during the hours of darkness for two main reasons, firstly journeying on or off shift, and secondly in pursuit of pleasure, as recounted next:

> *'I went to the Lyric Theatre – they had some wonderful shows on in the evenings – I was walking back up the road and there were hundreds and hundreds of Germans walking with their jackboots clattering along the road. My cycle light was a jam-jar, half full of earth, with a little night light in it, with a bit of box cord hanging from the handlebar, you see. I was walking along this cobbled gutter and the string came loose and the jam-jar fell in the gutter and the light went out. There were torches everywhere, with the Germans wondering what was happening. I pretended to know nothing about it, I just walked on leaving the night light in the gutter.'*

This is a humorous account of an accident that could have had much more serious consequences if the occupying forces had been in an aggressive mood, or indeed, if the flames had landed other than on the earth.

Other tales were told of embarrassing falls and fearful journeys as noises in the bushes sparked the imagination of the young women as they travelled in the countryside. Most of the spooky noises were the animals in the fields, but occasionally it would be a troop of soldiers from whom they fled. Their bicycles also took them to the more restrained and relaxing pastime of sunbathing. The two hours off in the daytime during the summer months was well used, and the natural gifts of Guernsey's beaches and sunshine were a bonus that they took advantage of with great readiness. Although, perhaps even more incredulous to the individual of today, is the fact that they would come off night duty and go swimming. Remember that they had only one day off each month:

> 'We went down to Vazon after we'd done night duty. We went down and had a swim. We shouldn't have, but we did. We laid on the beach in the sun, and 2 or 3 of us couldn't sit down for 3 or 4 nights afterwards – we'd got so burnt. We were lying on the beach and of course pulled our bathing suits up, you see.'

They had to be careful to avoid Matron or Sister knowing that they had suffered in the sun, since they would be far from sympathetic, rather they would have been in trouble for not going directly to bed and resting in time for their next shift.

The bicycle also took them to the cinema, where they saw some old films several times and took in the weekly German newsreel. So it seems that the need to entertain and be young and joyful about life helped people to stay resourceful and vigorous. Hard work has never prevented the young from enjoying life and this is evident in the lives of the Guernsey nurses. They lived hard and also it seems, played hard. They found the means to enjoy each other's company, despite curfews and distance and overcame many difficulties to ensure that their leisure time was as fulfilling as their working life.

VI

Make-do and Mend

OF COURSE, THE PHYSICAL REALITIES of Occupation are legion and although the lightening from heavy anti-aircraft fire could be absorbed and used as unintended assistance, the necessary commodities of healthcare were soon to be exhausted and no replacements easily ordered from 'Supplies'.

The example of the lamps previously alluded to, projects a lasting image of the ingenuity that nursing staff had to show to maintain their caring services.

Power cuts became a regular feature of life during the Occupation. When the lights went out, other means of illumination had to be found if patients were to be cared for through the night. Empty sauce bottles filled with inflammable oil, usually diesel, provided the basis for a crude form of light. A strand of cord from a pyjama girdle would be fashioned into a wick and passed through a hole in the lid of the bottle. A shoe-lace could also be used for this purpose. Initially, these pyjama wick lights would be lit from the Aga stove but would go out easily at the first hint of a draught, so the nurses would shield the flame with their hands. Relighting an extinguished light was done more easily from another

(opposite) **Outside Medical Ward E** (left to right – patients unknown)
Male nurse Len Downes, Nurse Martel, Staff Nurse Warne, Nurse Newman, Nurse Le Poidevin, Male nurse Napper, Matron Rabey (seated).

lamp and as there was only one to each ward, it would mean nurses going to another ward where hopefully they would find a viable light.

'If it went out you had to go to another ward to light it, and if in lighting it you put the other one out, you were in a right mess, weren't you? There was no torches.'

Although ingenuous in themselves, these small lamps were neither numerous nor infallible. They had to be carefully maintained and could cause some difficulties for the nurses who were forever moving from ward to sluice and back. Maintaining overall illumination of the ward could also cause problems:

'One day I dropped the lamp as I was walking.'

'If you had to go to the sluice with a bedpan, the ward was in darkness, and vice versa'

Fuel was so scarce that only one lamp per area or nurse was possible. If the nurse left the ward she would have to take the lamp with her, given that the black-out meant there was little in the way of natural light to help, so leaving the ward in darkness.

Beryl recounted that when shoelaces were substituted for pyjama cord, the fumes from the lamp sometimes caused breathing difficulties, as the chemical constituents of the laces burned aggressively and gave off noxious fumes. As the period of the Occupation lengthened, so the use of these makeshift lamps increased, with some surprising and other fairly obvious consequences. One nurse recalled a particular moment from a middle-of-the-night childbirth:

'Another time a baby was being delivered up in the ward and the lighting gave out. I had to hold a candle standing at her foot, you see. And as the baby was being born, blood shot out and put the candle out, and we were in darkness. These sort of things happened, but you took them in your stride.'

I suspect that early jocular cries of 'who put out the lights' became replaced with frustration as poor lighting became the norm and the continual tiredness of the times took its toll.

The nurses found that these mini oil lamps added to their difficulties with finding appropriate uniform, and created laundry problems for them. They would be covered in smuts by the end of a night shift, particularly on white caps and aprons. Those who worked in the nursery found that in the morning all the babies had smuts on their noses as a consequence of having been fed in the night by the light of the little lamps. All patients experienced this 'smutting' to some extent.

So even the modest 'Vick' or paste jars found an essential use in the recycling processes that became a feature of this period. Despite the inconvenience of carrying lit jars, there is a sense of romance expressed through the imagery of nurses moving about their duties amidst the bobbing of firefly-style lighting. Certainly, the smiles of the nurses as they recounted their memories of these lamps were smiles of affection, mellowed by the practicalities of the experience.

A *Wartime Soap?*

The need to 'make do and mend' permeated all aspects of life. As there was also a shortage of soap, there was a particular lack of elegance to the feelings of managing hygiene needs under trying circumstances, cleanliness being a major imperative of nursing then, as now. A soap shortage is a serious deficit in the nursing world, where hand washing and care of the hygiene needs of others predominate. The well-known saying that cleanliness is next to Godliness was never truer than in the Emergency Hospital. In any hospital, patients have to be kept clean and nurses and doctors need to maintain their own personal hygiene, particularly to reduce the ever-present possibility of cross infection.

Initially, the acquisition of soap was not a great problem, as apparently a large amount had been purchased from various London sources before the war and hoarded away on Guernsey. This soap was discovered in the early stages of the war and sold cheaply to the hospital where it was stored and dispensed by Sister Stephens. There were different brands including Wright's Coal Tar and Sarnia Soap. French soap was also quite common, but gritty and harsh to the skin. One former nurse remembers her mother having a large amount of French soap that was kept in the loft of their house to dry out and thus last longer. French soap used in the hospital came in small, pale green tablets, and was hugely unpopular with the nurses:

> 'As you washed your hands, this cement-like stuff would come out into the water, goodness knows what was in it.'

Soap gradually became scarce and what remained had to be used efficiently. Theft of soap was treated seriously, and an entry in the House Committee minutes of 9th March 1943 illustrates this very well. The hospital secretary had reported that on 6th March, Sister Stephens had drawn his attention to pilferage of soap from the soap store. It appeared that 14 tablets of Wright's Coal Tar soap, 21 bars of Sarnia soap and 33 tablets of other brands were missing. It was thought that some person possessing a key had opened the store door. An extra bolt and padlock were fitted as a precaution against further pilfering. The civilian police were asked to investigate the incident, but there are no records of anyone being charged with the offence.

Patients' relatives would sometimes bring good-quality perfumed soap, containing olive oil, into the hospital and the nurses greatly enjoyed using this soap when giving patients their bed baths. One said:

> 'It was such a treat for them and for us. Our hands felt lovely and we felt good ourselves.'

The idea that providing pleasant care creates feelings of well-being for both patient and nurse is far from new, but still poignant, given the serious absence of ordinary pleasures available at this time. It is far pleasanter and considerably more rewarding to provide ordinary assistance for a patient using good-quality products. The feelings that were expressed about the 'concrete' soap made it clear that both nurse and patient did not experience the same sense of comfort and well-being.

Soap was not only used for personal cleanliness but for also ward cleaning, and small amounts were allocated to the maids for wall and floor washing. Male orderlies also found themselves engaged in this task, and Ossie has stories to tell about this aspect of his work:

'On one occasion when things were fairly easy, Matron (Rabey) wanted her ward properly cleaned. So she had her cleaning ladies there and as acting male nurse they asked me to carry on as well. So I was issued a very small piece of soap. Now out side the kitchen door was a sort of feature wall and fumes from the kitchen gradually deteriorated the paint and it was all badly discoloured, so Matron asked if I could improve it a little. So I did and improved a small area of the wall and she said "Oh can you do the rest of that wall?" I said "Sure" and off she went. Of course I was acting as male nurse as well, and she wanted me at the other end of the ward. I went along, having put the soap down carefully on the side of the bucket, tended to the patient, and came back and the soap was gone of course. I'm pretty sure a cleaning woman had put it in the bottom of her bucket but I didn't know and couldn't prove it.'

The story doesn't end there. Ossie recounts that he had previously noticed that in the place where the cleaners stacked their things at the end of the ward there were several bars of material, about 5 or 6 feet long, that appeared at first glance to be wood. Due to its weight, he had wondered what kind of wood it was and to his surprise closer inspection revealed that it was soap. He recalls:

'So nobody knew what it was, they all thought it was old wood covered in dust, you see.'

Where it originated is not entirely clear, but it seems that some time prior to the Occupation there had been an incinerator situated near the old tram sheds on the esplanade at St Peter Port which was used for the disposal of animal carcasses. (Currently used as bus and coach garages.) The resulting fat from this process was probably recycled into the manufacture of soap. Unpleasant smells emitted by this incinerator is well recalled by Beryl Ozanne and Barbara Newman. The source of manufacture of the soap is not accurately recorded, but there was a small soap factory located in the Truchot area of the island that traded under the name of Jones. However, there is no evidence to suggest that this particular product came from Jones's factory. What is known and recalled quite clearly by former nurses is the part played by a certain Mr Frank Le Page in acquiring and storing large quantities of this soap. To understand who he was and how he fits into the story, we turn again to the history of the original pre-war Country Hospital.

The hospital provided caring facilities for a wide variety of patients, including an annexe set aside for the treatment of mentally ill men. The hospital also boasted a thriving farm, including a herd of dairy cows, several substantial gardens and a host of outbuildings. Mr Frank Le Page was the manager or 'master' of the farm and gardens, assisted by his wife Gladys. The farm and gardens provided work for some of the more able-bodied inmates of the psychiatric annexe, and also some female workers, who by all accounts were worked extremely hard by the 'master' and his wife.

Mr Le Page was alleged by the hospital authorities to have been a dealer in black-market goods including soap, which he kept in an area that was later to be used as a store for cleaning equipment. Apparently, Matron Rabey spent a great deal of time trying to keep an eye on the activities of this rather unpleasant man and his wife, but she also had a hospital to run.

It is unclear whether Mr and Mrs Le Page were ever caught in the act of black-market dealing and the nature of their eventual departure from hospital employment is unknown. Whether they retired or were dismissed remains subject to speculation. However, their legacy of soap was very welcome to a hard-pressed Ossie, and the dairy herd provided a valuable source of milk for the patients.

Ossie recalls that the soap hidden in the cleaners' cupboard came in various shades including blue-veined, marbled, white and sometimes red, so when he needed soap there was plenty to go at. He cut a piece of soap from one of the bars and completed his task of cleaning the wall. Owing to his secrecy in not divulging the soap cache, he was accused by Nurse Rhoda Leale a 'no nonsense' highly respected nurse of long experience – of taking it from the anaesthetic room, in fact she had reported this to the Ward Sister. In his defence, Ossie had to disclose his hoard which was then promptly removed to the laundry where it was put to good use.

He recounts another story about cleanliness, this time it concerns polishing the ward floor. It seems that one particular cleaner every 2 or 3 days would spread huge swathes of polish on the red composition floor, but did not bother to rub it in, thus leaving a hard, ridged surface. It became Ossie's task to level out the surface and along with three other staff cleaners he would spend a great deal of time on his hands and knees polishing the floor. Ossie recalls that the floor became packed with polish and it was very difficult to deal with. One particular instance is recalled in his own words:

'When Matron came on her rounds I was still doing it *(polishing the floor)*. *It wasn't very nice and Matron didn't like it a bit. She told Nurse Leale and Nurse Leale told me:* "Matron says you're very good on the ward but she wishes you were a little more efficient at polishing the floor". *I couldn't very well make a fuss about it as I was only there on sufferance'*.

What Ossie meant by this was that as far as he was concerned his main role of Acting Male Nurse took precedence over other more menial tasks. However, because Matron herself had asked him to polish the floor and scrub down the feature wall he would have found it very difficult to refuse either job, but to say that he did it with good grace is debatable.

VII

The Hospital
Caterer's Lot

POOR LIGHTS AND AN ABSENCE OF SOAP featured high on the tales told about these five years, but the hospital authorities were to the fore in trying to manage the use and allocation of scarce resources. Of course the various committees did not engage in this rationing themselves, they created positions to administer their policies. One such post was that of the Hospital Caterer.

The saying that a 'policeman's lot is not a happy one' can quite easily be transferred to the work of the Emergency Hospital Caterer. Although a thankless job, it was a key appointment, deemed to be a nursing responsibility, and carrying the title 'Sister'. The Hospital Caterer during the Occupation was Sister Stephens who by all accounts was a fiery and formidable woman who we shall see, did not suffer fools gladly. She was appointed to the post on 1st January 1941, being literally thrown in at the deep end. The main qualification for the post was that the incumbent 'shall have had experience in catering and cooking'. Her responsibilities were listed in the Emergency Hospital Mandate and included the supply of provisions as well as the efficiency of cooking arrangements for patients, nurses and other persons entitled to have meals in the hospital. Sister Stephens was accountable for the cleanliness of the kitchens and all related

(opposite) Group photograph in the Hospital Garden (date unknown).

offices. She also had responsibility for the punctual delivery and quality of meals in all departments of the hospital.

Sister Stephens had to check the accuracy and weight of all supplies, and she was empowered to use her professional judgement to reject provisions that were substandard. Similar to the Matrons she had to report her actions on a weekly basis to the House Committee or Hospital Secretary. She was responsible for keeping accounts relating to all provisions or other articles within her department, checking all invoices against delivery notes. Her role was combined with that of dispenser, she assumed responsibility for maintaining sufficient stocks of dressings, bandages and other material resources used within the hospital.

In her role as trouble-shooter, Sister Stephens would refer to the relevant matron any questions that may have arisen in connection with the food, diet or service in the wards or nurses' home. Where problems could not be resolved these were taken to the House Committee for discussion. All meals supplied to patients and nursing staff had to be agreed by the Matrons. It was this aspect of her role that caused some local difficulties, particularly when the Occupation began to take hold and food became scarce. The relationship between Sister Stephens and the Hospital Cook was not always harmonious, particularly when complaints were received regarding food that was poor in quality.

A good example of these 'in-house' difficulties was illustrated at a meeting of the House Committee on 12th September 1944, when a complaint was heard regarding the supper served in the hospital on the previous Thursday. The President of the committee had seen a sample of this meal and had to admit that it was 'pretty bad'. At this juncture

Sister Stephens was admitted to the meeting and was informed of the complaint. Her response was that the bubble and squeak served for supper on the night in question consisted mostly of cabbage. She had spoken to Mrs Adam, the cook, and discovered that she had allowed a kitchen girl to mix the vegetables instead of doing it herself. The ensuing altercation between Sister Stephens and the cook led to Mrs Adam stating that she was leaving, which Sister Stephens felt to be a good idea. Upon Sister Stephen's departure from the meeting, Mrs Adam was admitted to give her side of the story.

She said that she had always given of her best but was tired of the continual grumbling. Even though she admitted that the supper in question was not good, in her defence Mrs Adam said that Sister Stephens had instructed her to use up all the cabbage, which had it been served with butter sauce would have been palatable.

As it was, because she had followed the Caterer's instructions the meal was very poor. She further complained that the kitchen maids would not take orders from her as they state quite openly that Sister Stephens was in charge. Dr Sutcliffe thought this was wrong and that the cook should be in charge of the kitchen staff and give the orders direct.

The cook was given a weeks holiday to reconsider her decision to leave. Sister Stephens was recalled to the meeting and left in no doubt who controlled the kitchen maids and who should give the orders. In essence, she was given a dressing down by the President of the committee and told not to overstep her already considerable authority.

However, it is quite easy to see how such a power struggle could arise because Sister Stephens had been given the onerous title of 'Chief of the Hospital Kitchen' and all duties carried out by kitchen staff came under her jurisdiction, with additional responsibilities for overseeing laundry and sewing room staff. Sister Stephens had the power to engage and dismiss kitchen staff and female domestic staff subject to report and approval of the House Committee.

Male staff employed in the kitchen service were not entirely part of her empire. Instead they were engaged and dismissed by the Hospital Secretary after consultation with the Caterer. Within her broad remit she had an additional responsibility for securing the premises at night and was placed in charge of the house keys. As if this was not enough, Sister Stephens would also act as Theatre Sister in the event of an influx of air-raid casualties.

By modern standards it would seem incomprehensible to invest this range of responsibilities and power in one person. It becomes even more incredible when one considers the unique conditions under which she and her nursing colleagues had to work. The ring of military steel surrounding Guernsey completely isolated the island from mainland Britain and to a large extent also from France. Although limited supplies of medical equipment and soap found its way in from the continent, wholesome food was always going to become scarce.

Poor diet, overwhelming infection and transmittable disease took an unacceptable toll on patients and in some cases also on nurses. For example, diabetic patients present their own special needs and at a time of scarcity these may be difficult to fulfil.

On 18th May 1943, Sister Stephens reported to the House Committee that the weekly supply of eggs to the hospital from the Island Provisions Committee was 10 dozen, and this was insufficient to meet her patients' needs. Her request for an increase to 12 dozen fell on deaf ears, the argument being that there was little point in stabilizing these patients on food that was unobtainable at home. The Committee also cut meat and cheese rations to the same group of patients. Potatoes were also rationed to a weekly amount of 5 pounds per head. The plight of diabetic patients is graphically recalled by Ossie who, because of his ambulance responsibilities, was able to see the effects of malnutrition in the community as well as inside the hospital.

He was on duty one night when he noticed a patient in the medical ward who was his second cousin. He looked very ill, so ill that Ossie thought he was dying. Ossie greeted him in Patois, the traditional language of Guernsey, asking 'how are you?' His cousin replied;

'I'm terrible, I want to die. I've lost one leg and they're going to cut off the other; it's gangrene, completely gangrene.'

Ossie was shocked by this so he just said; 'I'll see you in the morning' and went about his duties.

He knew that he would not see him alive again. This proved to be an accurate assumption because by the morning his cousin had died.

Former nurse Barbara Newman clearly recalls the dietary problems that beset patients and nurses alike although, as we shall see, the senior nurses seemed to fair better than the juniors;

'Milk was rationed of course. If you were a gastric patient or perhaps suffering from malnutrition, then you could have full cream milk. Otherwise it would be skimmed milk – we'd have 8-pint jugs, big enamel jugs full of milk that we had to eke

out, just giving the full cream milk to those who needed it. Otherwise it was a diet of little pig potatoes in their skins, spinach perhaps and dark-eyed peas that were as hard as you know what, nondescript gravy – oh it was terrible. If you were off in the evening and wanted your supper kept you could put your name on a slate in the kitchen where it would be kept between two plates on top of the Aga.'

Later we will learn how inventive the nurses and indeed the Islanders became in creating enjoyable meals out of what would be regarded today as scraps, which perhaps before the war would have been fed to the pigs. Anyone who has exerted themselves in any form of heavy work (which nursing undoubtedly can be) will realise how important and at times all consuming the need to eat can be.

Stoicism aside, the human body can be difficult to manage if hunger wins, as the survival of the Islanders during this time required strength, not just in body but also in spirit. There is little that can reduce the spirit so quickly as the move from being well nourished and having freedom, to feelings of continuous observation and hunger. The experience of hunger can lead to character changes and just occasionally the compliant young nurse can and does rebel. This became evident on one occasion when feelings of injustice were experienced at the end of a hard day, particularly as suspicions were raised that senior personnel had abused their powers. Such a dark thought was prompted by savoury smells wafting from the kitchens, as recounted next:

'I complained to one of the dining-room maids that "it was that rubbish again, can't we have fish and chips like the Sisters?" – because we could smell the good food frying – we never had anything fried. I stood on a chair and looked over

the glass partition (it was frosted at the bottom, clear at the top) and there they were, eating fish and chips with part of our ration of fat. I said as much to the Hungarian maid and she reported it to the caterer. When I came back one night she (the caterer) said, "Nurse, I don't wonder that you want to have food here, would you like your ration book and you can feed yourself?" ...which of course was quite impossible, so I just had to knuckle down and like the food, and that was it'.

Even by today's standards this is an unhelpful response and far from caring, since a young nurse was essentially being threatened. The split between the layers of the hierarchy was very evident in this example, and perhaps exposes negative aspects of the bureaucratic management structure. A fortuitous reminder, some may think, before we jump on the bandwagon of returning to the 'good old days' when matrons, doctors and nurses knew their place.

~ VIII ~
Rationing & Health

THE SENSE OF SMELL is highly significant, the comfort of good aromas and warmth bring with them powerful memories that help people make comforting associations at times of need. The one aspect of night duty that did seem to have some attraction was the fondness with which everyone remembered the old Aga stove. These stoves were highly practical, as they would burn anything, a feature that became even more essential as the war continued, with traditional fuel supplies becoming less available. The Aga stove provided heat during the long winter nights, it was a place to cook the nurses' supper and heat up the patients' drinks. The smells of even the most barren of menus could make a cold and miserable night bearable. As the nurses said:

'It was very warm there, with the Aga, yes.'

'Warm in front of the Aga, yes.'

'I can still picture it.'

'Yes, so can I.'

The cosy glow that emerges from the descriptions of the night shifts huddled around the Aga form a romantic memory and can belie some of the privation of these times. The combination of cold and hunger, constantly felt, cannot have been a comfortable experience particularly when constantly on the move. It is in our nature to recall the good memories rather than the harsh realities of privation and frustration; the picture of warm friendship around the Aga is one such recollection. Even in these descriptions of trying times the situation of the patient was not far from their thoughts. Trained to serve others and put their patients needs before their own they knew that their 'Aga picnics' could have consequences for those 'outside the blanket', so to speak, as the smells of cooking pervaded the ward. The nurses would screen the Aga stove as they cooked their meagre rations, often potato skins brought in from outside.

> 'We had a screen around the Aga.'

> 'I mean, even if we had potato skins.'

> 'Well, they were selling potato peelings in the market for three-pence a pound, would you believe it.'

A meal of potato skins and gravy that is remembered as though it could have been a nourishing and wholesome dish underlines the extent to which the senses, in particular smell, has an impact on the experience of hunger and nutrition.

So, on night duty, not only did the nursing staff have to provide care for the patients in the cold and dark, but also if they were to have anything to eat themselves they had to cook it. Hence the therapeutic memories of aromas and huddles around the Aga. Of course the cook was important in the conversion of such constrained ingredients into nutritious and filling food. Burnt offerings would be far from a joke when rations were as scarce as they became in the final years of the war, so the choice of cook was important, perhaps it was also a popular task in that at least the cook was warm. Certainly there was no canteen on night duty, and the menu does not sound as appetising to modern ears as the fond memories seemed to indicate:

> 'They used to send the raw ingredients in big enamel dishes, with potatoes that may or may not have been peeled... I used to do the cooking when I was on night duty always.'

> 'But you did what you could with the food. You might have a dish full of gravy, and you'd boil the potatoes, maybe put them in the oven and they came out quite tasty. All sorts of funny things like that.'

Other replacement foodstuffs needed some treatment before their senses found them acceptable. Versatility in cooking methods required even more ingenuity. No healthy cooking in olive oil here, rather the stuff that is more familiar in preserving the willow of cricket bats found a recycled life as cooking oil.

> 'We'd fry with linseed oil, which you boiled and put a clove of garlic in it to take away the linseed taste.'

> 'That's right.'

Even simple things that we take for granted required careful thought to maximise availability to the whole population. Such activities did not depend entirely on individual initiatives, but the work of the Controlling Committee contributed immensely here, in particular the management of the imposed rationing. Even water was rationed; people would have to keep turning on their taps at home just to ensure that they collected some water during the short periods when it was turned on. The hospital had its own water supply and generator, but still experienced shortages and power cuts, as highlighted earlier. So the need to make do and mend did not end with the recycling efforts, but also impacted on daily nursing activities that ensured that waste was minimised – a sentiment frequently echoed today as the budget constraints of healthcare provision are realised. Perhaps the realities of this early privation could reassure nurses of today that bad though their circumstances are, the constant availability of 'the bare necessities of life' can and does make a major difference. The final months of the war were particularly difficult, as one nurse recalls:

> 'Of course we didn't have anything in the last few months, no gas or electricity.'

> 'Well we did at the hospital, but at home there was no...[gas or electricity]'

> 'Electricity and gas were rationed, I remember. We had a gas meter for the oven, but there was nothing else – gas was 8d a week, old pennies, you know, these big copper pennies. And my mother used to have 8 pennies literally near the meter. Once that was finished you just couldn't have any more gas that week, so it was a good way of saving.'

Good was seen as coming from the bad; it would help in contributing to the savings necessary to re-establish themselves once the occupying forces had left their Island. The need to find ways around the rationing was evident throughout the accounts from these times. It would be a disservice to the people who experienced these times if the rigours of Occupation were not addressed here. The heroic and often humorous episodes that contributed to the maintenance of morale and the ability to provide nursing care would be incomplete without some exploration of the effects of deprivation.

RATIONING AND HEALTH

On an Island such as Guernsey, cut off from the mainland, the potential for self-sufficiency is limited. The healthy and strong may survive but the weak and frail, already vulnerable, are put at risk by inadequate diets and a lack of special foodstuffs. The food and energy rationing had an impact on the nature of the patients, as those with special dietary needs like diabetics and the elderly had very difficult times surviving in this climate. Maintaining diabetic patients often proved difficult as a balanced diet is essential in these cases.

> 'The diabetics suffered. We got them infrequently, didn't we, before D-Day. I don't remember any diabetics on either of the wards after D-Day.'

The Occupation lasted five years, so the early months and even years seemed more 'normal' than the final half of the Occupation. Gradually, the population reaped the consequences of a continuous poor diet, which had some serious consequences for their health:

> 'I think if you hurt yourself, it didn't heal as quickly as it would have done normally.'

> 'We didn't have much at all, did we? It got used up.'

The nature of the patients that they cared for changed over time. Slowly, the weaker members of the population found that their resistance to minor infections was reduced and recovery delayed or as in the very frail (as the quote above explains), they died. The medical authorities and the management committee of the hospital realised the effects of malnutrition and patients were cared for longer periods on the wards than was the norm even then. When asked about this, former nurses recall the extent to which patients were kept in their beds. The value of milk in offsetting malnutrition was also commented upon:

'Much longer.'

'Because we had the milk to give them here. I think the milk saved them. I mean, we had so many with malnutrition coming in and, well, they had milk a few times a day, didn't they? And it helped them tremendously.'

So patients were recognised as having special needs from the early days. The special dispensations gained through the various controlling committees for the hospital were used to the advantage of the most needy.

Additionally, there were many severe burn cases in the final year as fuel shortages led to an increased use of home-made lamps, with many accidents causing horrific injuries.

'Do you remember the little boy who was brought in – very badly burned.

'Do you remember that Christmas we were together on children's ward? With 8 children split up on each side, and we played skittles. There was a boy named Gordon who had a set of skittles from Father Christmas.'

'Gordon, yes, how did he get so badly burned?

'I can't remember but I know he was very badly burned.

'I know a boy called Edward was – there was a fire in the house and his brother, his smaller brother was in it; he went in and rescued him. That was when he got burnt from rescuing his younger brother.'

Making the best of the circumstances brought out the best in the Islanders. Few and far between were any detectable memories of unpleasantness as a consequence of deprivation. Rather their shared experiences resulted in heroic acts on the part of both children and adult citizens, almost as an accepted part of life. There were a number of stories about individuals who had rescued relatives from fires and this prompted us to enquire about the frequency of burns. It was no surprise that a definite connection existed between the frequency and severity of burns and the rationing of electricity or gas for lighting. The use of home-made lamps was common throughout the Island and not just a feature of the inventiveness of nurses on the wards. Open fires used to light, heat and cook within the home caused many serious incidents, as they recalled when asked about the frequency of burns caused by home fires:

'Yes, quite a few, because the normal conditions for providing heating and lighting weren't there.'

They recalled one patient who was seriously burned and the length of time she was in the hospital:

'Seventeen months she was with us.'

Managing the care of burns patient must have taxed the ingenuity and determination of the nursing and medical staff.

The need to maintain sterile dressings and provide good hand-washing facilities for the nurses caring for such patients must have been a strain on limited resources. The nourishment of a long-term patient with such a debilitating condition also caused additional problems that extended the stay of these patients in the hospital. It was important for the benefit of the patients that they receive the additional food that their in-patient status allowed them, consequently, stays in hospital were often longer than was usual as convalescence outside the hospital meant that their extra food stopped. However, this was not the only factor that extended the stay of patients with severe burns, secondary illnesses that are evident even today, such as pneumonia, were a danger to the lives and well-being of long-stay patients. One particular example seemed to portray all the sadness of that time in relation to the dangers of fire:

> 'Yes, because you had open fires, and she went to get what she thought was paraffin to boost the fire up, and the can she picked up was petrol. Her mother was in an armchair near the fire, but she slung her mother out. We had her in for fire burns..[daughter] she was burned from waist down.'

> 'She was in a dreadful state, but she survived.'

> 'It's a wonder that she did survive.'

> 'I don't know how many times she had pneumonia.'

The care of people who were hospitilised for a lengthy period of time created bed management problems, an aspect of care service management not unfamiliar today. The combination of increasing bed occupancy, general deterioration in the health of the population and poorer healing powers as the war and the Occupation continued, meant that wards became crowded, space being at a premium. As a consequence, every space was used including the outdoor verandas, which had those special properties in relation to the German gun emplacements we mentioned earlier. The nature of nursing care, however, went beyond the tasks and the medical needs of the patients. These people who experienced extended stays in hospital became special and merited acknowledgements from all staff, irrespective of whether they were involved in their care or not. The following extracts indicate the extent to which nurses, whether from medical, surgical or maternity, became part of the care dimensions of long-stay patients:

'Although I wasn't on that ward nursing her, I saw a lot of her.'

'We always passed her bed when we went down to dispensary'

'We couldn't fail to see them.'

'When they were on the balcony, you sort of passed them. They all liked chatting to various nurses.'

As is evident from this conversation, there was a need for nurses to develop skills of caring that encompassed the spiritual, emotional and social energies of living. Perhaps, it is through experiences of caring in such circumstances as these that nursing theorists evolved and identified the need to promote the holistic nature of nursing work, and in particular the gentler paths of caring. For them to emphasise only the physical, in times of dire shortages, would have reinforced the deprivations of rationing. However, despite the deprivation nurses found a great camaraderie of spirit that memories of the aromas from the old Aga continue to fortify.

Waste Not Want Not

When listening to stories of malnutrition and disfiguring injuries caused by a lack of basic necessities, the fast food emporiums of today seem to belong to a different world. There are many examples of the ingenuity with which the Islanders managed to overcome some of the dietary deficiencies. Some of these former nurses remembered bramble tea with fondness and acorn coffee with shudders. Other recipes included parsnip coffee, carrot cake and pudding, and karigeen moss made into an almond-tasting jelly. So there was much enterprise shown by the (re) invention of natural food recipes to supplement their diet.

The Channel Islands are famous for their potatoes and tomatoes, and although the German troops controlled the farms and greenhouses, the one food that seemed to last the length of the Occupation was that old staple – the potato. Even the humble potato was insufficient to sustain the people alone. The nurses had to rely on warehoused stocks of dried food such as macaroni and rice. By the fourth year of the Occupation these food-stuffs were beginning to take on a less than appetising appearance.

Earlier, we remembered inventive ways of creating recipes that used natural ingredients and acted as replacements for proprietary brands, such as bramble tea. Now, as the Occupation took full effect on the Islanders, the dried foodstuffs that seemed endlessly available in times of plenty were beginning to suffer the effects of unexpectedly lengthy storage times. Those sacks of dried pastas remaining were considered essential nourishment for the staff and patients of the Emergency Hospital. The fact that they were now 'alive' with crawling creatures was insufficient reason for rejecting them, but even here the fortitude of the day came to the fore, exemplified by the ribald laughter of our nurses as they recalled how they responded to the introduction of maggots into their diet:

'Extra meat!'

'I just pushed mine aside.'

'And we used to count them, how many we had round the dish.'

'We didn't look to see what was inside the tube.'

'We turned a blind eye to anything that moved.'

'When you look at the four of us even, I mean, we survived.'

'We're very lucky, aren't we?'

Breakfast was also an adventure. The porridge oats were not of the best quality, containing maggots and full of husks. Even milk seemed to be different at this time, particularly as it was mainly reconstituted powdered milk. Weevils and maggots, being stoical creatures, found a dousing in cold liquid not too distressing. It was the hot liquids that brought them scurrying and wriggling out of tubes and visible to the human eye:

'They had maggots in the oats. We used to make porridge of oats, it was all husky and you used to have to sift the maggots out before eating the porridge.'

'And then when they put on the hot milk, which was like blue water, all the weevils came out. I took a spoonful before I realised they were weevils.'

Human nature being as it is, the general population thought that perhaps food would be better in the hospital than it was at home. One nurse, having just taken up post 18 months into the Occupation, approached her first breakfast with some relish having noted that there were rusks or cereal-based biscuits to be served with milk:

> 'When I started at the Hospital, I remember the first breakfast – a rusk in each dish. I thought that's marvellous, you know. Until you sat down, and it was covered in web. God knows where those rusks came from.'

Harold, one of the 'inmates' from the psychiatric annexe, was often referred to with fondness as he helped the nurses in many ways. This man of gentle demeanour contributed in his own way to making mealtimes and the preparation of meals a little more appetising:

> 'He was a nice chap, wasn't he? Sort of quiet and kept to himself. I needed a lot of help in the kitchen, and he'd help the girls by lifting all these big urns.'

> 'He was the one I saw skimming maggots off the top of the macaroni.'

> 'Off the top of the milk.'

> 'This was before it went in the milk.'

Hence the fond remembrances of Harold who had helped in removing the less savoury items from the simmering brew before any attempts were made to make an appetising dish.

The robust nature of a nurse's stomach is legendary. One need only eavesdrop on lunchtime conversations to experience the disregard nurses have for the 'gentler' conversational subjects more usual over meals. It was not given to everyone to manage such a diet, even in the extreme deprivation of this time. Malnutrition was a problem and if individuals could not accept the foodstuffs that were in poor condition then their health suffered additional insult. It is important to realise that malnutrition was an increasing problem from as early as February 1942. As one nurse quietly added:

> 'Well I wasn't a fussy person, but my mother was very fussy and she lost an awful lot of weight.'

The serious nature of the deprivation experienced during the final years of the Occupation is truly realised in accounts such as this. These nurses not only experienced first hand continuous hunger, which could be relieved only through eating what seems to be noxious food, but also had to support patients who experienced the same maggoty diet. Food parcels from home must have been a major source of energy for patients and a serious contribution to their strength. They all had memories of parcels, whether they came from the Red Cross on the good ship *Vega* (described later), through the occasional mail drop, or from the good services of Raymond Falla a Guernsey man of some influence, who was well respected by the nurses:

> 'The cheese, the French cheese running out of the boxes. My mother used to queue up for that. Oh god, it was awful – the smell!'

> 'Oh, I loved it.'

> 'We all ate it.'

They shared with us tales of gorging when the food parcels arrived, that is until the nurses learned the hard lesson of a little and often being better than eating a whole chocolate bar after their 'fasting' diet (relative to today's standards). Of course we must not misconstrue the notion of gorging, when what is meant here is the consumption of a chocolate bar or a tin of condensed milk, rather than extreme overindulgence. It was just that they had become used to austerity and their bodies found rich food difficult to manage when suddenly introduced:

> 'We got our Red Cross parcels as well, my cousin and I, we had this coffee cream… We were a bit greedy, I'm afraid, and we had to go on night duty that evening. And she was very young. If you haven't had food, rich food… It was too rich, you see. I couldn't take it… It was just a small tin… She was so ill.'

> 'I'm not surprised.'

> 'I did the same, you open up the tin and have a spoonful, don't you. And you think, oh just one more… And there's one more, and there's one more! Before you know where you are, you're feeling ooooaah. I'll never forget it… I had to stay in the bathroom all night, with a bed in the bathroom. Too much all at once, see, after so much, not having had sugar for years. The next morning I had to go to the office, and I had a good telling off from Sister Clayton for being greedy. No sympathy. And you said to me, I've seen the angels this time. Oh, I was bad, I was really bad.'

Even in times of deprivation the professional rigours were imposed and foolish behaviour was no excuse for failing to attend to duty. It is interesting that feelings were expressed more forcefully over the memories of illness due to overeating and the recollections of the maggoty meals portrayed with humour.

Earlier, we describe how humour, allied to a youthful sense of fun, contributed to their survival; even in these austere times, life had to be kept in perspective. After all, maggots were an alternative source of protein!

Use and use again

It was not only in the catering department that deprivation was experienced and improvised strategies established to overcome these. The practical items needed to achieve the daily tasks of nursing and manage successful care practices were also scarce. Today, there is a major growth in disposable equipment, both in the home and the hospital. Not so in an occupied country where the most ordinary and taken for granted aspects of a comfortable life could not be replaced. As Barbara Broadbent remembers:

> 'There was no such thing as use and throw away. It was all washed, cleaned, disinfected and used over and over and over again.
>
> 'Very strong disinfectant.'
>
> 'Lysol, was it?'
>
> 'Everything was sluiced, of course, no matter what was used...'

The empty Vick and fish paste jars came into their own again as receptacles for thermometers. We asked about the penalties for breaking a thermometer, recalling our own early training when a breakage resulted in an interview with Matron. We felt chagrined as we were met with the astounded response that things did not get broken, and care was taken, as replacements were almost impossible. The Emergency Hospital Committee minutes reflect concerns about excessive breakages in the maternity wing and, indeed, they required Matron Finch to account for this. Her response was that in her opinion breakages were 'mainly due to carelessness'. A somewhat typical response from management perhaps. Our interviewees did not make up the entire staff of the Emergency Hospital, but were obviously exceptional in their practices and standards of care.

Another area that is taken for granted today is the use of gloves when carrying out many procedures. They were certain that such luxuries would have been considered redundant:

> 'We didn't have gloves. I don't remember wearing gloves.'

> 'No, never saw gloves.'

> 'We used to sluice the draw-sheets and things like that. We weren't wearing gloves because there weren't any.'

> 'No, only the doctors used gloves, well, only in the theatre.'

You will recall the saga of the soap earlier and the difficulties in providing simple personal care measures, such as washing, in a pleasant way. These constraints extended to the laundry and created difficulties in providing everyone with the necessary clean linen. The minutes of the Emergency Hospital House Committee are interspersed with decisions made to alleviate the problems the hospital management faced in providing many of the 'hotel' services that are part of routine hospital care. For example, earlier in the book we describe a decision made by the House Committee on 19th August 1941, regarding the care of dental patients. These patients, who had traditionally remained in overnight, should either bring in their own sheets or be cared for as day patients only and nursed on a mackintosh or blanket, so saving a sheet.

Bringing in your own linen seems a strange state of affairs today, but then there were other precedents that made this seem a fairly sensible thing to do. In maternity, it was the norm for baby supplies to be brought in by parents and the laundering was the responsibility of the father. One nurse who started as a very young probationer at the age of 16 recounted how she managed the task, ensuring the washing of nappies through a system of individually initialled bags:

> 'In those days you had to collect the nappies and there were about twelve pegs in the sluice. It was my job to wash out all these nappies, which was not very nice, tidy them up and put them back in the individual bags, Because in those days they all had their initials on the nappies and the bags, so I was able to match them up. They would then be hung on the pegs. When the husbands came in the evening they'd take their little bags home; that was most useful.'

We asked if they took nappies home to wash.

> 'Yes, nothing was washed at the hospital, they only took them home and brought them back the next day. That was their little laundry bag. Being a junior that was my job'.

By using the resources that each had in their own homes they contributed to the management of the scarce hospital resources.

Towards the end of the Occupation clinical necessities became scarce. Simple commodities such as wound dressings were unavailable, the make do and mend approach came to the fore, rescuing the situation yet again.

> 'I can remember a time when we ran out of all sorts of dressings and cotton wool. The hospital asked people if they had stockings or car seats and things like that, to sterilise as medical padding.'

Early on the Emergency Committee, advised by nursing and medical staff, had been sufficiently far thinking as to secure sterilisers that could be used on the Aga stoves. Sterilisation by boiling seemed to be the best way of ensuring cleanliness, that and the ubiquitous Lysol. Resource inventive or otherwise, it takes imagination to realise the urgency of the plea for padding from car seats to be removed and given to the hospital to use as dressings for what were at times severe and deep wounds. Although with the petrol shortages it is likely that for many their car was a redundant machine.

Getting About

Walking and cycling featured as the principle means of getting about. It would seem that shortages of supplies would not impact on these modes of transport; if such were your reflection then you, like us, would be wrong. The bicycle was the most common form of transport and was frequently a source of deliberation within families as to who should have the use of it, irrespective of whose bike it had been before the war. Fathers who had to walk a long way to and from work would commandeer their daughters' bikes, which left them without the means to move around the island. The bike itself did not survive unscathed during this five-year period. There are many parts on a bicycle that wear out and replacements were not easily come by. The make do and mend philosophy came into force here also. By the end of the Occupation, we were told, there were no brake blocks to be had, therefore brakes were suspect to say the least. Tyres and lights were also scarce. It seems that bicycle tyres and the soles of shoes need constant repairs that gave rise to even more inventiveness on the part of the Islanders. The soles of shoes were patched using car tyres. If such extravagance was beyond you then the return of the Island clog was the only recourse. The lucky clog owner had leather soles with slits in to create a more flexible shoe; the less fortunate had stiff, loud, wooden soles.

'Before the war I had a pair of heavy walking shoes, and there was a shoemaker in Le Friquet called Troubeau. I would take them to him for repair and he'd put a piece of leather on. The shoes were almost all patches by the end of the war; They had a sort of composition rag sole and as you wore them down so the ends of the rags would come out of the soles.'

So, shoes were a problem and yet fashion consciousness had not slipped by these young women – just because there is a war on does not mean that anything will do! A pair of shoes finessed from some fortuitous avenue, but sadly an unfashionable white in colour, were quickly dyed using permanganate of potash, a lovely shade of beige, and so were worn with dignity and panache for the remainder of the war. Others raided the attics of their older and frugal relatives to find hoarded treasures that could be used, dismantled and re-made or, where all else failed, used to patch and mend a favourite article.

Shoes rather than dresses were the main theme of the discussions about clothes, perhaps a reflection of the length of time they spent toiling on their feet going about their daily nursing duties. They were certainly reduced to minimalist approaches to uniforms by the end of the Occupation. Each nurse found herself wearing some form of motley clothing rather than a traditional uniform. This ranged from an old Guide dress to assorted collections of best dark dresses to patched and altered uniforms handed down by retired relatives.

To end this section there can be no better words than those of one of the nurses who said:

> 'You got used to it, you see, of taking care and making do and mending'.

~ IX ~

Tragic Tales

Nurse Theresa Steiner (third from left), who worked at the Emergency Hospital, was deported during the occupation and died in the Auschwitz-Birkenou gas chambers.

WHEN WE ARE ASKED TO RECALL our past lives, it is no surprise to find that the easiest memories are those that were pleasurable, being recounted without pain. Even the stories of hardship, presented in the previous chapters, have been remembered with a rye humour and recounted with a quiet dignity. As this group of nurses talked and regained the feelings of comradeship and youthful zest they began to think about some of the sadder times. It is not possible to nurse without experiencing tragedy, particularly during a time when families were separated and the presence of an 'enemy' felt in everyday events.

Among the many stories told to us by former nurses of the Emergency Hospital there are those that recall events of sadness and tragedy. It would be remiss of any account of the Occupation and nursing to omit the story of Theresa Steiner, and here we have the opportunity to add a human dimension to her tragic tale. Two other aspects of a sorrowful nature that follow are those of the potential severity of childhood illness and the personal experience of death when nurses become ill and die.

THERESA STEINER

The deportation and execution by the German authorities of Theresa Steiner aged 26, Auguste Spitz aged 40, and Marianne Grunfeld aged 29, came as a great shock to the nurses in the Emergency Hospital. They as others in Europe found it impossible to believe that any nation could with deliberate intent end the life of an individual based on their 'race' and religion. We should, therefore, place this story that follows in the context of that time and prevail upon ourselves to remember that the understandings of the last 50 or so years have just begun to emerge. Indeed, it is evident from current world events that racial hatred and suspicion continue, the absence of effective learning from the past a tragedy in itself.

The story that follows involves three people – Theresa Steiner and Auguste Spitz, both born in Vienna and Marianne Grunfeld born in Kattowitz, Austria – all three women were of Jewish nationality. Theresa had previously trained as a dental nurse in her homeland, subsequently working as a ward nurse at the Emergency Hospital, where Auguste (known as Gustie to her friends) worked as a ward maid. Marianne was locally employed as a farm worker on the Duvaux farm, Baubigny, St. Sampson's. She was not registered with the Guernsey and German authorities as Jewish, but the others were, the letter 'J' being stamped in red on their identity cards. Although Theresa Steiner and Auguste Spitz worked at the Emergency Hospital for a relatively short time, their story forms a vivid memory in the minds of former nursing colleagues.

The tragic tale of their deportation and demise is well documented by Frederick E Cohen in his book 'The Jews in the Channel Islands during the German Occupation 1940-1945'. Together with his accurately recorded account, and the personal recollections of former nurses, we will follow a journey over those eventful months that resulted in Theresa Steiner, Auguste Spitz and Marianne Grunfeld being among the first deportees from Western Europe to eventually suffer execution in the Auschwitz-Birkenou gas chambers.

How Theresa came to be at the Emergency Hospital is the subject of various reports in the *Guernsey Evening Press*. Following the Nazi takeover of Austria and the rise in anti-semetic behaviour her family, fearing for her safety, sent Theresa to England. She was one of the few Jewish refugees to be allowed into Britain, and secured employment as a nanny in the household of Edgar and Marjorie Potts who lived in Beckenham, Kent. Mr Potts was a dentist, his family included two young daughters, seven-year-old Wendy and five-year-old Angela. In 1939, the Potts family moved to Sark were they took a holiday lease on Rosebud Cottage. In 1940, Mr Potts returned to England to tend his business, his wife and daughters stayed for six months and greatly enjoyed the lifestyle offered by this small but beautiful island. The children attended the local school and Theresa continued to work as their nanny. Due to her Austrian nationality, Theresa was technically an enemy alien who had to register with the local police in Guernsey, agreeing to tell them of any change of address. The family then moved to another holiday lease at St Peter Port, because Mrs Potts felt that her daughters' education would be better served in Guernsey.

When it became clear that France was on the verge of collapse, the evacuation of the Channel Islands began and the Potts Family prepared to return to England, it was planned for Theresa Steiner to accompany them. She dutifully informed the Guernsey authorities of her impending change of address. However, this was not to be, as she was forced to remain in Guernsey, being interned under a Home Office 'enemy alien' regulation.

A story published in the *Observer* newspaper on Sunday, 12th May 1985, suggests that a local police inspector, who had already imprisoned about 30 other 'enemy aliens', added the young nanny, Theresa, to his list of prisoners. He did this despite her vigorous protests that she was a Jewish refugee who had already lived in England for a year previously. The report goes on to say that eleven days before the Germans occupied the Channel Islands, eight of the detainees were escorted to Southampton and the others were freed from custody. A number of these people, including Theresa Steiner and Auguste Spitz, were subsequently released and both women gained employment at the Emergency Hospital. Theresa formally registered as a Jew on 30th April 1940.

Both were popular with their nursing colleagues. Matron Rabey, in particular, is reported to have held Theresa in high esteem. She was a cultured young woman who, apart from being a good nurse, was an accomplished musician, playing the piano quite brilliantly. The nurses recalled how she had played for many of the concerts they produced for their own and their patients' entertainment. Despite the apparent ease of relationships between the occupying forces and the Islanders in the early days, it was only a matter of time before the German authorities were to impose the harsher regime of the invader. The change in the relationship, underlined to some extent by the story of Theresa Steiner, is remembered by all who survived those times. In particular, the fateful day when she was taken by the German authorities is etched indelibly upon the memories of those who worked with these young Jewish women. Mary Ogier recalls:

> 'I can remember sitting at the dining table, you know the nurses' dining table. She (Theresa Steiner) was sitting opposite me and she said, "All my life, because of my origin, I've been persecuted." Then they suddenly took her away, didn't they, and she died in the gas chamber.'

There are few times in peoples' lives that imprint themselves to the extent that individuals can remember exactly what they were doing at a significant moment in time. Beryl Ozanne remembers clearly that she glanced out of an upstairs ward window, providing herself with a vantage point that gave her an unforgettable view. It was the 21st April 1942, and printed in her memory is the image of Matron Rabey bidding a sad farewell to Theresa Steiner. The Matron must have known in her heart that she would never again see her alive.

Barbara Newman went with Theresa as far as the Weighbridge, St. Peter Port, but access to the quayside was denied by German soldiers – not even the Guernsey police were allowed that far. It was at the Weighbridge that Theresa met up with Auguste Spitz and Marianne Grunfeld, who were also destined for deportation. They were permitted to stay together for only a short time before boarding a boat for France. A stark statement in the House Committee minutes of the 21st April 1942 records the event:

> 'The President then reported that two members of the staff, Miss T Steiner, a nurse, and Miss A Spitz , a maid, were under orders from the German Authorities to leave the Island.

It was resolved to record an expression of regret at losing their services as their work had been of the highest order.'

Life at the Emergency Hospital went on, patients had to be cared for and nurse staffing levels maintained. To this end the House Committee continued their comment on the deportation of one of their young nurses, who had worked so diligently as a member of the care staff, 'It was further resolved that Matron Rabey endeavour to obtain another nurse to replace Nurse Steiner.'

The Matron did precisely that and one week after the departure of Thereas Steiner, on 28th April 1942, reported to the committee that she was 'suited' with a nurse Miss B Quevatre, who would make an admirable replacement.

The journey of Theresa and Auguste from Guernsey to Auschwitz-Birkenou was a staged affair. Originally, it is thought they believed their deportation would take them only as far as France, then moving on to Poland, but this was not to be. Having left Guernsey they stayed for a time in Laval where Theresa found accommodation in a residential area, and it is reported that she once again worked as a nurse. Auguste and Marianne were taken in by the Evron order of nuns who ran a local hospice.

In mid-July all three were arrested and transported to Angers where, deprived of all valuables and personal belongings, they began their fateful and final journey via the Drancy concentration camp, near Paris, to the horrific Auschwitz-Birkenou death camp. The final leg of the journey from Drancy began on the 20th June 1942, when, along with many hundreds of other Jews, they were locked inside hermetically sealed cattle wagons and taken by rail Convoy

No.8 to meet their respective deaths on 23rd July 1942. The appalling suffering during this journey can hardly be imagined. The manner in which they died is one that can scarcely be believed in the present day. Theresa Steiner's good humour, her balanced outlook on life is recalled. A final comment is expressed in a tone that even fifty years on speaks of disbelief:

> 'She was a lovely girl. It was so sad, that people could do that just because she was of Jewish origin'.

This story does not quite end with the war and the Occupation. Barbara Newman, aware of the momentous nature of this incredible event, although at the time not truly aware of the imminent death of her colleague, kept her possessions safe:

> 'I was the one who had all the stuff she couldn't take with her – her clothing and music. She had books of music which she obviously couldn't take, and I kept them. I didn't know what to do with them. Then her brother suddenly swam into the picture from Canada,...I went to America last year and stayed with them overnight on the way back. He was a Professor of Music. Theresa told me she had two brothers that were pianists, one was working in France and the other in China. This was the one who was in China. The one in France was liquidated along with Theresa'.

At this point the atmosphere in the room began to be solemn, and discussion faltered as memories that had been dormant for almost half a century were re-absorbed and put into perspective. The final whispered words of 'so sad' were almost too quiet to hear.

DEATH ON THE WARD

The next section in this tragic theme again features death, but perhaps in a more familiar guise for those who have nursed, or indeed for anyone aware of the nature of illness and the care of people who have life-threatening ailments.

Within our modern frames of reference it is easier to accept the death of elderly people, although there are occasions when even such a death can seem 'out of time'. Certainly there were many memories of older people who found that the restricted diet reduced their resistance to infection and who died earlier than would have been expected. The inability to live their final years in relaxation and comfort must have added to the feelings of despair that stemmed from malnutrition and debilitation. One nurse recalled how her grandfather died half way through the Occupation. He is described as a 'wiry man', so it is unlikely that he had reserves of strength as the rationing and impoverished diet began to take its toll:

> 'I'll swear my grandfather died of malnutrition. I'm sure he did. He was a very wiry man to begin with, but when I look back now I think, well, he just went down and down and down. He was taken in to the medical ward, down the stairs. And he died in 1943.'

The nature of death caused by malnutrition is one which we, in the affluent world, do not have ready experience. Even regaled as we are by images screened directly into our living rooms by television, through news footage and documentaries, these second-hand experiences encourage us to distance ourselves from the harsh and traumatic realities that exist in what seems, at times, like another world. Not so for these nurses, still of young and tender years, with little practical experience of the world outside of both their families and the relatively small island of Guernsey. They were required to manage horrific burns, experienced by both children and adults, and premature death in their compatriots. One nurse provides an example of the way that they perceived the poor diet to impact on individuals:

> 'I will always remember a man who died of a carbuncle on B Ward. He had a carbuncle on his neck, which became quite infected and it finished up that he died. I thought, what a horrible thing to die of a carbuncle. Malnutrition again, you see, no resistance at all.'

Yet even now in remembering sad and often tragic moments, the stoicism that ensured they coped with the demands of their daily role was highlighted again. If the cause of this suffering was lack of nourishment then what could they do? The hospital was able to keep some of the milk cows that pre-war had provided essentials for their kitchens, and the Emergency Hospital Committee ensured that in-patients were allocated additional milk. Thus patients were admitted perhaps for reasons other than 'medical' care, since one of the criteria for special consideration for food and in particular milk was being an in-patient. So although some died there were many that did not, saved by the insurance set up by extra supplies and their admission to hospital. At least such was their belief in the way that decisions to admit vulnerable individuals were made:

> 'Because we had the milk to give them here. I think the milk saved them. I mean, we had so many with malnutrition

coming in, they had milk a few times a day and it helped them tremendously.'

At the other end of the age span the very young were vulnerable, particularly during gestation and in those early first days. Again there was recognition of the need to protect the expectant mother through the ration books and a special milk allowance. The birth of a baby with a severe deformity was remembered as causing great emotional distress. The management of such births seems as problematic then as now:

> 'I was on the labour ward and it was a doctor's delivery. He said what was coming, and we were all appalled. We didn't want to say what we saw – the baby was born without a cranium and it was so difficult to tell the mother. We left the baby in the labour ward for a long time, thinking that it would pass away, but it was a healthy little baby. In the end we had to feed it on sterile water, cover it well so that the mother wouldn't notice what was wrong. It died about 10 days later'

They remembered the babies that had died in their care, though not numerous, each death was an individual tragedy, felt by all those who made even slight contact with the parents and nurses. The death of a mother was a major trauma and only one such incident was recalled.

There was much sympathy expressed even fifty years later for the nurse who had had to face this ordeal. The main sense expressed at this point in the recounting of their memories was one of sorrow, even now, for those who grieved, and of wonder that such examples were not greater given the difficulties faced by all.

However, set against all this, their memories emphasised the recovery rate as being high despite these emergency conditions. The need for the Islanders to work together to minimise the deleterious effects of the Occupation is exemplified in the co-operative enterprise of maintaining the hospital, as recounted throughout these personal tales. These stories of the fortitude of a small group, made up of mainly young women, must be considered in the light of the worsening situation as the years of the Occupation extended into the fourth and finally fifth years.

~ X ~

The Final Months of Occupation

FOLLOWING ALMOST FIVE YEARS of Occupation the situation on Guernsey was deteriorating rapidly. Towards the end of 1944 the allied forces had retaken Normandy, effectively isolating a whole division of German troops numbering 35,000 men within the Channel Islands. A fuel crisis had developed at the Emergency Hospital during October 1944 resulting in acrimony between members of the two governing committees as to whose fault it was.

A letter written by Dr R.E. Gibson to the Hospital Committee, deprecating what he thought to be a lack of insight regarding the fuel situation, was urgently discussed and refuted. The President of the Hospital Committee, Jurat John Roussel, remarked that on the 18th November 1944 information was received that the German authorities had released 20 tons of coke for all public services. His committee had endeavoured to obtain a part of this allocation for hospital use, but had been unable to receive a satisfactory answer from the Fuel Controller.

Emotions were running high, the Hospital Committee was looking to apportion blame. A letter drafted to the Health Services Officer brought to his notice the seriousness of the position, forcibly pointing out that should such a thing

(opposite) **Celebrating Liberation**
Matron Rabey and the Medical Ward staff – July 30th, 1945.

happen in future whilst fuel was still available, the consequences must rest with the Fuel Controller, not the committee. Experiments were carried out using tar fuel to fire the boilers, but because special equipment needed for the purpose was not immediately available the experiment proved to be less than satisfactory.

This did not alter the fact that as Christmas approached and winter was setting in, it became apparent that stocks of food, clothing, fuel and medical supplies were virtually exhausted. Fortunately, help was at hand. Were it not for the timely delivery of essential medical and food supplies by the Swedish International Red Cross ship, Vega, arriving from Lisbon, Portugal on 27th December 1944, the extent of suffering would have been markedly worse. The Vega paid further visits to Guernsey during February, March, April and May 1945, literally holding out a lifeline to a population that had endured so much.

During January 1945 the German authorities cut off the electricity supply, initially between the hours of 9am and 1pm, then later after 4pm also. However, a concession was agreed that power could be restored in the case of an emergency, providing due notice was given beforehand. In the case of immediate emergency, the generating plant at the hospital could be used. Petrol to run this generator had to be requisitioned from the civil reserve, with a maximum of 10 gallons being allowed for this purpose. Soap rations also caused concern, as all that remained of this precious commodity was a limited supply provided through the Red Cross. This was divided between the three Matrons who in turn were responsible for allocating it to the wards and nursing staff.

In the early part of February 1945, House Committee members became concerned that worsening conditions in the hospital would cause nurses to leave their posts. Dr Sutcliffe suggested that the Nursing Service should be considered 'National' in much the same way as the armed forces. Under this ruling, enforced by the Civil Duties Law, nurses would be compelled to continue their work and not permitted to leave. The Island Labour Office brought this Law into force and a Nurse Smith, who did attempt to leave, was actively prevented from doing so although she was permitted to work part-time.

These were desperate times because by the end of February 1945 there was no electricity supply to maintain the hospital at night; petrol reserves were seriously depleted and fuel for the boilers was running out. Paraffin lamps maintained ward lighting, but this was not a permanent solution, as the meagre supply of fuel for these would be exhausted after a short while. Without electrical power and effective heating patients would suffer and some could possibly die, as the operating theatres would be put out of action. Dr Sutcliffe considered making application to the Germans for a restoration of the electricity supply, but his request apparently fell on deaf ears. Surrounding trees were felled, split and delivered to the hospital for use in the stoves and boilers, which again was only a temporary measure.

If this wasn't enough, and despite the Civil Duties Law, Matron Finch and Sister Clayton had decided they could no longer carry on and offered their resignations to the House Committee. The hospital could ill afford to lose these key maternity nurses whose drastic action was instigated by a serious deficiency in the allocation of adequate domestic help. A sub committee investigated their grievance and it was agreed that the caterer be instructed to supply more domestic help to the maternity ward. Domestic duties would include the cleaning of the matron's, sisters' and nurses' rooms to the satisfaction of the matron herself. Three maids were appointed and as far as Sister Clayton was concerned this seemed to resolve the situation. Matron Finch was allowed to take two months holiday in lieu of notice and eventually left the hospital on 30th April 1945.

The hospital fuel crisis had by now reached a critical point and an emergency meeting of the Hospital Committee was convened on 10th April 1945 to discuss the situation. The 'make do and mend' philosophy so successfully employed by the nursing staff throughout the Occupation had permeated the committee itself. Novel ideas for reducing the effects of chronic fuel shortages were urgently explored. Even the faithful Aga stoves were in danger of running out of fuel and were it not for their wood-burning capability this would certainly have happened. Wood fuel in these particular stoves reduced their heat-producing efficiency as well as requiring that they be refilled three times in 24 hours.

Due to the dangers associated with undercooked food, a decision was taken to stop using Aga stoves in the kitchen. More efficient means of cooking would be explored. It was considered to be important for the stoves in the wards to remain alight using wood fuel, but they would not be employed for cooking patients' meals; eggs being the exception.

Whilst not wishing to add insult to injury, Miss Carey, a committee member, reported that she had recently lunched at the hospital in the matron's and sister's dining room where no one had eaten the beans. These were swimming in water, the cabbage was unappetising, and whilst some potatoes were whole others were cooked to a smash. She thought the food was badly cooked, badly served and most unappetising. Also the chief grievance seemed to be the awful monotony of the meals.

Former nurses echoed Miss Carey's comments:

'The worst part was having to serve up the meals that came from the kitchen to the patients – you had about a tablespoonful of mashed swede just plonked in the middle of a huge plate.'

'Jerusalem artichokes, I remember.'

'I remember when there was no potato, just vegetables, and you'd think, "Oh the poor patients". Some of the patients would say, "They're keeping all the good stuff for the nurses". They'd make us feel awful but we had exactly the same. You'd go down to the dining room and we had exactly the same food as the patients.'

None-availability of coal or coke meant that alternative forms of cooking and heating the food had to be found quickly. Obtaining a military field kitchen from the German forces being one suggestion, whilst others included portable coppers to be installed in the hospital yard, and domestic hot plates loaned to the hospital by individuals. Dr Gibson offered to provide a hot plate and Mr Laine, the States Engineer, would be requested to install the coppers. The President agreed to organise a supply of wood for the Aga stoves. So, as the old saying goes, 'where there's a will there's a way'. Dr Fox said that he knew an 'expert man', who could be employed to look after the regular refuelling of the Aga stoves during the day, although it would remain a nursing responsibility to keep the stoves alight during the night.

It is clear that throughout the period of Occupation, hospitals in Guernsey and neighbouring Jersey absorbed a share of a diminishing resource. This became more acute as the Occupation entered its final desperate months, but no one would begrudge the sick and dying the treatment they needed. The measure of suffering and privation felt by the ordinary civilian population typified this period in the history of the Channel Islands. It was responsible for much of the illness and accidental injury that befell many of the ordinary people. Earlier in the book, we described the horrific burns and overwhelming infection suffered by some of the patients cared for in the Emergency Hospital. Their poor physical condition was directly related to the living conditions that they were forced to endure, as one nurse from this period said:

> 'If we hadn't had the Red Cross parcels I think a lot more people would have died'.

The extent of human suffering throughout the Channel Islands during the Occupation can be judged from the content of a letter written by 'An Englishwoman in Jersey', published in the *Picture Post* on June 2nd 1945. She vilifies the oppressive German army and the black market that encouraged unscrupulous traders to charge well over the odds for essential commodities, thus adding to the poverty and deprivation. There are also well chosen words directed at the privileged few and towards women who willingly worked for the enemy. She says:

'Yet for the women who would not work for the Germans and had no official relations or friends, and for their equally loyal men, it has been more than a thin time, with privation increasing to complete cessation of food, fuel, light, clothing, boots, medicines, soap. During three months the Red Cross has kept us alive with Canadian and New Zealand prisoners-of-war parcels.

The fireless winter has been terribly cold. The wood ration, dwindling till it stopped, had to be saved for boiling a little water and trying to dry the men's clothes, soaked in weeks of incessant rain. We have raked over and carried away in sacks and bags the coal refuse flung out by the Germans. We have burned the doors and woodwork of empty sheds and houses and for so doing have been sent to prison. The soup of the communal kitchens has been very weak. Offal, fat, bones, dripping, oil, everything of which we heard and for which we enquired has been 'sent to the institutions'.

Sea-water has been placed in the town streets to give us salt, and a charge of a penny made for it. We have sat in the dark, been ill in the dark, risen in the dark and under all circumstances our toil of work has been the same, and official tempers and manners in warmish offices, have been the reverse of civil'

Picture Post Vol. 27 No.9 page 3.

As the desperation became more acute, prisoners held by the Germans for the purpose of enforced labour roamed the locality in search of food and shelter. A former nurse remembers how frightened she was of these unfortunate people:

'I wasn't frightened of the Germans but near the end of the war I was more frightened of the labour – because they were *hungry, they were starving. I was a bit nervous of those people, because they used to escape at night looking for food'.*

The German soldiers suffered in much the same way as the civilian population, and Beryl Ozanne recalls that troops would steal anything edible from houses, fields and gardens. The few remaining household pets were hidden, otherwise they too would finish up in the German cooking pot. The German forces did not divert Red Cross parcels for their own use, but once in the hands of Islanders the parcels would be vulnerable to theft and were kept hidden from the view of soldiers on the hunt for food. The human need to survive was never more forcibly illustrated than in the Channel Islands at this time. People were reduced to eating rabbit skins and making soup out of nettles and cabbage leaves. Malnutrition was a very serious problem and liberation had to come quickly or the consequences would be too horrific for words.

LIBERATION AT LAST

The news of Adolph Hitler's death on May 1st 1945 cheered the Islanders and the Union Jack appeared in public once again. An expectation that liberating forces would appear in the next day or two was gaining ground and the people were not to be disappointed. It was at 3pm. on May 8th 1945 that Prime Minister Winston Churchill delivered his now famous speech to the nation in which he made direct reference to the liberation of the Channel Islands:

'Hostilities will end officially at one minute past midnight, Tuesday, the 8th May, but in the interests of saving lives, the

'Cease Fire' began yesterday to be sounded all along the fronts, and our dear Channel Islands are also to be freed today'.

Winston Churchill's speech was greeted with enormous relief and public emotion ran high. Many people who heard that speech remember exactly where they were at the time. One former nurse clearly recalls her location:

'I heard it in the nurses' dining room. We'd gone down for a meal and there was this big broadcast at 3 o'clock in the afternoon to say that our dear Channel Islands would be freed today. Well!

And to think we could be out all night if we wanted to! No curfew-that was so important.'

On Wednesday 9th May 1945 at 7.14am, a very stubborn Vice-Admiral Friedrich Huffmeier, the German Commander in Chief, eventually surrendered the Channel Islands to the Allies, seven hours after the official ending of the war in Europe. The German surrender was accepted on board HMS *Bulldog* anchored off the Channel Islands, from which an advance party landed in St Peter Port the same day. During the afternoon, HMS *Campion* and HMS *Cosby* arrived carrying British troops who began the task of liberation. A group of soldiers from the Royal Corps of Signals made their way to the Emergency Hospital with food for the children. Barbara Duport recalls:

'...and then when the British troops came – you know when we were liberated – they were rushed up to the hospital with tins of biscuits. They were only old, great big thick army or ship's biscuits, but, oh, didn't they enjoy them!'

Night nurses, billeted locally, having slept all day came on duty that evening unaware of the momentous events happening in St Peter Port Harbour. They discovered that liberating troops had landed only when day staff living nearer to the action rushed back to the hospital, where they spread the good news to staff and patients. One former nurse recalls this quite clearly:

'I was on night duty. Gwen, another nurse who worked with Beryl, went home, they lived in King's Road and I remember her coming back to say that the British had landed'.

'No one knows how you really felt, you just can't explain'

Emotions felt at that time are rekindled very easily. Memories and feelings resulting from five years of oppression are not easily eradicated, as illustrated by one of the nurses when reliving liberation day:

'It was 5 o'clock before I came off duty that day, and the harbour...'

She couldn't finish describing the scene that greeted her, but words were unnecessary as the emotion in her face told its own story.

Liberation brought a boundless joy to the nurses, doctors and administrators of the Emergency Hospital, but they had to carry on regardless. The aftermath of enemy Occupation would result in a continuation of serious health problems requiring skilled nursing and medical care. Despite the hospital moving into a period of 'altered conditions', there remained many difficulties to be addressed and surmounted.

HELP FROM CANADA

Nursing shortages continued to plague the hospital and an immediate plea for assistance was met by the Canadian St. John Ambulance Brigade, who dispatched four nurses to work at the Emergency Hospital. A/S Alice Holland, A/S Iris Moore, A/S Pat Standish and C/O Clarice Ogden arrived in Guernsey, coincidentally at the same time as Herbert Morrison, Minister for Home Security, who visited Jersey and Guernsey on the 14th and 15th May 1945. During this time, Herbert Morrison toured the Emergency Hospital where he assessed the depleted resource situation for himself.

Beryl Ozanne has fond memories of meeting and working with her new Canadian colleagues who she describes as 'delightful and enchanting'. She recalls with a rye humour how resplendent and pristine they looked in their uniforms when compared with the Emergency Hospital nurses, whose uniforms Beryl describes as 'drab and grubby'. After five years of making do, mending and having to make things last far beyond the time when uniform dresses and aprons would normally be replaced, it is little wonder they appeared dowdy and grey.

The Canadian nurses stayed at the hospital for about a year, where they contributed enormously to the rehabilitation of a nursing staff that had suffered years of Occupation-imposed incarceration. They were the first outside nurses to enter the Emergency Hospital for five years, bringing news from around the world. They introduced new ways of nursing to a group of locally recruited staff that had come to rely on tried and trusted methods for so long. In so doing they contributed greatly to the comfort and care of patients. Their contribution was recognised over fifty years later when Sandra James, a Guernsey Senior Nurse, visited Canada in June 1997 to deliver a paper at the International History of Nursing Conference held in Vancouver. She took with her a letter from the Sir Graham Dorey, Bailiff of Guernsey, addressed to David M. Johnson, Chancellor of the Canadian St. John Ambulance. The essence of this letter was to thank the Canadian St. John Ambulance for help and assistance offered at the time. In replying to Sir Graham's letter, David Johnson wrote:

'On behalf of the Priory of Canada please accept my sincere thanks for the honour you bestow on St John Ambulance. There will be many who remember, as if it were yesterday, the nurses who served in Guernsey'.

August 12th 1997

During the post-occupation period of altered conditions, the Emergency Hospital slowly returned to its peacetime role and it became clear that a fresh supply of nurses would be needed to support and replenish the service. A letter sent to V.G. Carey, Bailiff of Guernsey, dated 25th August 1945, from the Lieutenant Governor's Office, set out the need to assess the trained nursing situation across the Island. The letter concludes as follows:

'To be constructive, may I ask you to give your approval to my asking Home Office to arrange for the visit of some experts from the Ministry of Health to Guernsey to consult with your own Medical Advisers and the Local Medical Practitioners, and try to work out a plan which will enable you to draw on one or more of the big training hospitals in England for your supply of trained nurses, and to make any other

recommendations for the reorganisation of the Islands'
hospital services as their experience may suggest to them'.

This letter may have had the desired effect because a number
of Guernsey women, who had spent the war years training
and working as nurses in the United Kingdom, returned to
the Island. Some of these nurses found employment at what
had now become the former Emergency Hospital, and
continued the process of introducing new ways of doing
things in the form of treatments and therapies. There was
some amazement and amusement levelled at nursing
practices employed during the Occupation years but, as Beryl
points out, they were five years behind the times.

It was no surprise, however, to find that years of 'making
do and mending' had equipped the Occupation nurses with
ward management skills that could only be envied by the new
comers. Beryl takes great delight pointing out that in spite of
the incoming nurses' up-to-date ways, the Occupation nurses
were still able to show them a thing or two in the day-to-day
running of the wards.

Having come to know and admire these resolute women,
we have absolutely no doubt that this was the case!

Postscript

Senior Matron Ella Elizabeth Rabey.

I T SEEMS FITTING TO END THIS ACCOUNT of nursing during the German Occupation of Guernsey with a tribute to Senior Matron Ella Elizabeth Rabey who was finally able to retire, tendering her resignation on 29th June 1945. However, Matron Ellen Hall, who was to succeed her as senior Matron, went on holiday and the President of the Emergency Hospital Committee asked Matron Rabey to take charge until Matron Hall returned. Matron Rabey left the service in the Autumn of 1945 and received a glowing tribute from H.W. Cochrane, secretary to the Emergency Hospital Committee who wrote:

'Dear Matron

On the eve of your departure from the Hospital I should like to convey to you my sincere thanks for all the help you have given me during the past 5 years.

We have been through very trying times for all, but you have always done everything possible to help and for that help I am deeply grateful.

That you will be missed is certain but you have the love and esteem of all, and you have certainly earned a well deserved rest. May you long enjoy that rest.

I will say au revoir only as I hope we will continue to see each other, and with every good wish for your happiness Believe me to be,

Yours very sincerely

H.W. Cochrane.

31st August 1945.

Five years of Occupation made enormous demands on the physical and psychological stamina of the Emergency Hospital nurses who, through real dedication, kept the torch of care and compassion burning brightly during the darkest years of Guernsey's history. At the very heart of this dedication and devotion to patient care could be found a strength of purpose reminiscent of Florence Nightingale herself. Ella Elizabeth Rabey was the source of this strength, who by her selfless example inspired a group of inexperienced and largely untrained young women to become highly effective nurses in conditions that today's nurses could not even comprehend. The Nightingale maxim of 'to do the patient no harm' became deeply ingrained in their very being, remaining with them long after they too had left the service.

Ella Elizabeth Rabey began her career at the London Royal Free Hospital in July 1914. This was the beginning of a life of service to the sick spanning 50 years, many of which were in positions of clinical seniority, culminating as Senior Matron at the Guernsey Emergency Hospital. Despite achieving this level of seniority, she never left the bedside and would regularly roll up her sleeves, working shoulder to shoulder with the regular medical ward staff. Matron Rabey's immense contribution to the work of The Emergency Hospital resulted in it becoming a monument to the dedication and skill of a truly remarkable person who gave so much of herself to the people of Guernsey. The hospital still stands – if only its walls could speak!

Long after retirement she continued to give service to the St. John Ambulance Brigade, and in July 1948 accepted the commission of Nursing Officer in the Guernsey Cadet

Division where her influence would, once again, guide the future career of many aspiring young nurses.

In her latter years she lived quietly with her brother and sister at 24 Mount Durand, St Peter Port, where incidentally she had lived as a small child. Matron Rabey died on 31st December 1960, one month short of entering her 79th year. A plain headstone in the Island's Foulon Cemetery marks her final resting place.

We can say, with certainty, that the nursing profession will never see the like of Ella Elizabeth Rabey again.

ACKNOWLEDGEMENTS

We are grateful to the following people whose help and guidance enabled us to write this book.

The staff of the Guernsey States Archive Service;

The Librarian and staff of the Priaulx Library, St. Peter Port, Guernsey;

Senior Nurse Sandra James and staff of Catel Hospital, Guernsey;

Major Edwin Parks, formally a reporter with the Guernsey Evening Press and now with Channel Television.

Rachel Rabey and Jane Wilson, nieces of Matron Ella Rabey;

Helen Scott, Editor of the British Journal of Nursing, Mark Allen Publishing, for granting permission to reprint extracts from the article by Peter Birchenall.

Curators of the Guernsey and Jersey Occupation Museums for their expert guidance.

Margaret Dalton for her skill in transcribing the interview tapes.

Jill Tyldsley for her critical reading skills.

BIBLIOGRAPHY

Baum W K 1970 *Oral history for the local historical society*. Presentation at a seminar of the Oral History Association October Harrisburg PA

Birchenall, P. 1997 Nursing in Wartime Guernsey: a preliminary review. *British Journal of Nursing.* 6:22:1315-1322.

Briggs, A. 1995 *The Channel Islands – Occupation and Liberation 1940-1945*. Batsford. London.

Cohen, F.E. 1998 *The Jews in the Channel Islands During the German Occupation 1940-1945*. The Institute of Contemporary History and Wiener Library Limited in Association with the Jersey Jewish Congregation. Jersey C.I.

Falla, F. 1981 *The Silent War*. Burbridge Ltd. Guernsey, Channel Islands.

James, S. 1997 *Nursing in Guernsey During the Occupation*. Conference paper presented at the International History of Nursing Conference, Vancouver, Canada. June 1997.

Johnson, P. 1976 *A Short History of Guernsey*. Distributed by Guernsey Press.

Leale, J. Rev. Jurat 1945 *Report of Five Years of German Occupation-an address to the Statesmen of Guernsey*. Reprinted from the Guernsey Evening Press. This publication represents a review of the 5 years of occupation and was intended to provide an account of the stewardship of Guernsey exercised by the Controlling Committee. Whilst there is no indication who reprinted the document, it is authentic and was published the *Guernsey Evening Press* shortly following the Liberation.

Moriarty, Dorothy. 1989 *Dorothy: The Memoirs of a Nurse*. Corgi Books. London.

Ozanne, B. 1992 *A Peep Behind the Screens 1940-1945*. The Guernsey Evening Press Co. Ltd. Guernsey. Channel Islands.

Parks, E. 1992 New research shows local Jewish women sent to Auschwitz. *Guernsey Evening Press.* 18th June:3.

'An English Woman in Jersey.' – May 9th 1945. Letters to the Editor. *Picture Post* June 2nd 1945.

RECOMMENDED FURTHER READING

Boleat, Peggy. 1993 A *Quiet Place*. Villette Publishing Limited. Guernsey.

This autobiography represents a rare glimpse into the life of a patient during the German occupation of the Channel Islands. Peggy Boleat, a Jersey woman experienced a long period of time recovering from tuberculosis, resulting in two years of hospital care between 1941 and 1943. In this case the setting is Jersey but the experience of Occupation was much the same as on Guernsey and this well written book provides the reader with fascinating insights into life from the other side of the screen.

Ozanne, Beryl. 1992 *A Peep Behind the Screens 1940-1945*. The Guernsey Evening Press Co. Ltd. Guernsey. Channel Islands.

This book provides a highly personalised account of nursing during the Occupation of Guernsey. It is a store-house of memories, some of which are laced with rye humour and others that reflect the rawness of the time. Above all it is a book that demonstrates the essential spirit of nursing that shines through the darkness and dangers of caring for people in an occupied war zone.